RAMBO

7 SEASONS AT SAINIK SCHOOL

RAMAKRISHNA

INDIA · SINGAPORE · MALAYSIA

ISBN 979-8-88629-261-9

Dedicated to

My Parents for giving me absolute freedom to be myself

&

To all my fellow Saikorians for making me who I am.

Contents

Foreword

Sainik Schools take pride in transforming young boys into men; physically fit, morally upright and mentally motivated enough; to serve the nation selflessly. This transformation is not brought about by mere focus on organized studies and co-curricular activities but more importantly due to the unorganized *albeit* institutionalised peer group interaction. Seven years of value based military schooling with a set of friends rewires one's DNA in more ways than anyone can imagine. While separation from parental home in the early years of life is excruciatingly painful, the search for empathy amongst strangers bond them up to be brothers for life.

My first recollection of the author, fondly known as 'Rambo', was of an athletic personality walking past the portals of the education block in our Sainik School with an air of confidence unseen amongst the rest of us in the first year of schooling. Over the years, I have seen him handling many challenging situations in a mature and composed manner making him a natural leader. This book is about his journey with his band of brothers and how it has shaped him into what he is today.

Many books may have been written till date on the life in Sainik schools but this book is unique as it dwells into the various activities which a student is exposed to on a day-to-day basis, unbeknownst to any other premier boarding school, and how they help in evolution of the student's personality.

My congratulations to the author for his vivid account of every event of schooling creating nostalgic moments for the alumni. An inspirational read for students aspiring to be part of the prestigious alma mater.

Colonel Ganesh

Preface

As a child we are playful. As a teenager we are joyful. As an adult we become responsible. As we age, we become mindful. What we forget in the process is that we are the same person who evolved from a child to a teenager to an adult to the elderly. This ignorance makes us arrogant. Only a constant reminder of this fact can keep us grounded and free us from attachment and illusion.

What we see depends on where we stand. Our actions can have far-reaching effects. Their impact depends on how we absorb them. In our lives when we are engaged in living a pretentious life, we create an illusionary world of our own. However, sooner or later, we realize this and take charge of our lives.

This story is the journey of one such child – Rama alias Rambo - the story of him losing his identity, then finding it. It is a story of self-discovery that everyone can relate with - the story of how we become 'what we are' and 'what we are capable of'. Set in the tough environs of a Sainik School, it gives us a sneak peek into the seven years of boarding school that creates men with nerves of steel. It is the story of how Rambo adopts, interprets, and evolves from an innocent child to an arrogant teen, only to later realize his folly.

Hilariously witty, this book is also a fun read with adventure and profound life lessons thrown in good measure, in places where you least expect to find them.

Take charge of your life. Don't become its slave. Let sorrow feel envious of your joy, and let inspiration be inspired by your attitude.

Explore the journey of your life through Rambo's journey.
Always remember to:
"Live inside out"

Acknowledgements

Life is all about acknowledgements, no matter who we are. Just to imagine life in itself is blissful. The universe has set everything in motion to make us realize that we are the finite replica of the infinite Universe.

I take this opportunity to send out my heartfelt thanks to each and everyone who enabled me to complete this book, directly or indirectly. Without their support and well wishes, I could not have accomplished my dream.

In my journey of self-discovery, I have been blessed with parents who are the epitome of love, sacrifice, and compassion; my family who gave me my space to be myself; teachers who tolerated me and my ways; friends for being the source of my strength and confidence; and colleagues who are my constant companions.

I am indebted to my wife Haritha for being my pillar of strength and having taken up the huge responsibility of tirelessly taking care of our family, uncomplaining about my shortcomings and constantly inspiring me to do what I aspired to do. It's only because of her support; I have been able to pen this book down after procrastinating for two decades.

I thank Havish, my son, who is such a creative storyteller, one who pushed me hard to tell him more. Hope this book will serve to guide him in the future.

My beautiful little daughter Hayati, who infuses spirit in me to do better with her cute smile.

All my Saikorian friends formed the source of inspiration for this fiction. Without them and the experiences we shared together this fiction couldn't have become a reality.

My dear friends Maya and Ganesh for stretching themselves in reading the manuscript and giving their valuable inputs, insights, and suggestions to make it better.

A special thanks to my friend Ganesh for writing the Foreword.

My nephews Akhil, Abhishek, and Jeshwanth for being so supportive and encouraging.

My editor Laseeta for having owned the Book and infusing life into it.

The Notion Press publishers for having been so professional and cooperative.

And finally, life's circumstances that locked us indoors, and gave me time to write.

***Love You All and God Bless ***

How This Book Came About

This story has been living within me for the past two decades. I even wrote a few pages. Subsequently, I got busy with life and could not dedicate time to it. Though I gave up writing it, the book did not give up on me. It was at the back of my mind, no matter what I was engaged in.

I thought that if I could not invest time to write it, why not make a web series out of it? I pushed this idea to my brother-in-law who is into film production. He liked the context and premise of the plot and asked me to come up with a written script.

I laughed. It was lack of time that had led me to the idea of a web series, in the first place. Now, with the ball back in my court, it was my serve again. My nephew suggested a professional web-series scriptwriter. We discussed it with him. He found the plot so engaging that the following weekend; he arrived with his entire team! We planned to make a trilingual web series. However unfortunately due to better work opportunities, the team decided to move on without working on my project!

It was a rude awakening for me. I had narrated the story to them without even signing a Confidentiality Agreement. I felt uneasy. My wife understood my dilemma and suggested that I write a book instead of the web-series; *With the lockdown in force and time available, focus on the task and complete it; you might never get another chance.*

Never did I so relentlessly work for anything in my life. In three months, between challenging lock-downs, medical emergencies and office work, I had completed my book.

By August 2020, I had completed the first draft and was looking for an editor. Through my friend Arundhati, and Ms. Bhavana Nissima, I met my editor, Laseeta Kunhikannan. As I spoke to Laseeta I felt assured that my book was finally in safe hands. The content was now crisp and clear.

Maya, a friend agreed to do a beta-reading from a reader's perspective. I thank her for her kindness. My dear friend Colonel Ganesh, in spite of his busy schedule, wrote the foreword. I am grateful to you dear Ganesh. I thank my Publisher, Notion Press for creating such a wonderful cover and layouts.

"When the student is ready the teacher appears" - Lord Buddha. When I was determined to write my book, I met the right people who helped me accomplish it. Everything looks challenging until it is completed. I had written in three months, a book that I couldn't write in 20 years!

I bow down to Lord Rama for making my book a reality. But for You, this wouldn't have happened my Lord.

I hope you enjoy reading my book...

And that, as you read, you will go back in time, to your school days, and laugh and riot with Rambo....

And that, you will travel with him while he is Rambo and be with him in his journey of becoming Rama again.

| Chapter **1** | **Introduction and the Beginning** |

The Sun shuffled unhurriedly through white clouds.

It was about 4:00 pm.

The year 2001.

In a small village in South India.

Kondrapole.

On its way to set, the evening sun scorched everything it looked at. From where I was sitting, I could see people walking towards this part of the stream. I have been sitting there for the past five days - or was it seven? I don't remember. The postman comes this way by four usually. The bridge that I was sitting on, was built only a couple of years back; when the village officer wanted to drive his car to his house. It was the biggest bridge in the village. Only slightly bigger than the one close to my house. My head felt heavy with a million thoughts racing and pausing momentarily for my attention, I bent and looked at the stream flowing below. The evening sun cast my shadow on the water below. It flowed softly; most of it through the center of the stream. The canal overflowed when it rained. But now it ran slowly, almost threatening to stop and dry.

"Aren't, you quiet these days? What brings you here every day at this time?" It was Mahesh. He looked concerned.

I smiled wanly. *"The postman."*

"Oh really!!!"

"Yeah really!!!"

My ears heard a faint tinkle. Running towards the bridge, I saw him at once. On his cycle. Turning towards the bridge. It was indeed- the postman!

With another tinkle of the bell, he cycled past me. Chasing him, I called out, urging him to stop.

A pair of grey bushy eyebrows pointed inquiringly at me. We were standing near my home. The postman seemed amused to see me panting, trying to breathe and speak at the same time.

"What happened?"

"Nothing. I just wanted to enquire if you have anything for me?"

"Yes. There is a letter for you - from your school. But why do you look so nervous?"

"No! Not at all! I'm all good."

I quickly collected the brown paper envelope and ran towards my house.

Once inside the gates, I glanced around to make sure nobody saw me as I folded and slid the envelope inside my trouser pocket. My heart pounded. My lips moved softly in prayer. I walked towards my house pretending to be calm. I entered my room, hung my shirt on a peg and took a shower to calm myself. I was acutely aware of every breath I took, moving through my chest. I sat at my desk, with my hands folded. I tried to be brave. Then shaking my head, I got dressed, picked up the keys to the temple of my family deity - Lord Sri Rama.

On any other day, I could connect easily to the divine. Lord Rama always stood tall and steady, calming me in all my storms. I walked towards our temple; letter tucked inside my pocket. My hands trembled as I opened the temple doors. With blurry eyes, I looked into the eyes of my Rama.

Stepping over the wooden threshold I entered the temple. I raised my hand to ring the huge brass bell above.

Walking through the small mandapa, towards the sanctum, the cool marble floor tickled my bare feet. I opened the wooden door to the sanctum and peered inside. The scent of sandal, jasmine, and ghee[1] used in the morning pooja felt comforting. The brass lamp near the deity had a tiny flame.

I applied tilak[2] and with folded hands bowed before the Almighty. My eyes brimmed with tears as I looked at the Lord. Then kneeling, I placed the letter at his feet. Touching my forehead to the ground, I whispered, *"My lord! You have always been the source of my strength and confidence. But today, I confess that there have been times when I confused my over-confidence as confidence and acted out of ignorance thinking that I was being smart."*

"It's only now, after having completed my seven-year journey in this School, I understand how I have fooled myself. It's not that you aren't aware of my ignorant attitude. But I am terrified of its outcome now. Please take me through this, Lord."

Memories of the past seven years flashed as my mind wandered to the day when it all began.

It was about 4 o'clock, on a humid summer evening in the blazing summer of 1994.

I bit my lower lip in dismay as I lost another game of marbles. My friends were masters at the game and moreover, luck was on their side today. My box of marbles emptied faster than I finished chewing out the

---

[1.] Ghee- Clarified butter from Cows' milk
[2.] Tilak – sacred mark on the forehead

last bit of my fingernails. I looked pleadingly at Krishnaveni, my sister, a champion. *"Please play for me."*

She smiled back. *"What are sisters for?"*

I fervently prayed and as Krish poised to strike, I closed my eyes.

"Yeah! Yipee!!"

She smiled.

"A winner!"

"Bingo! On spot. As always."

"Awesome!" I yelled. *"You are mind-blowing!"* I hugged her as I filled my empty box with marbles again.

We stopped playing as a red bus passing by the dusty road ahead, stopped. It was coming from Miryalaguda (nearest town) and had stopped because someone was getting off the bus.

A euphoric-looking Thaku hopped out of the bus and ran towards us shouting, *"See what I've got! A new tape recorder."*

It was super amazing! Till now we only had a radio with a couple of channels. The songs were few and infrequent. Now we could play songs of our choice. In no time we were all at Thaku's house. Yelling and singing and dancing all at once, at the top of our voices.

Thaku was bombarded with song requests.

"Boys calm down and speak clearly. Which song should I play first?"

"GANGLEADER" - all shouted in unison- a chartbuster of our favorite Megastar Chiranjeevi[3].

Sensing the mass hysteria around the song, Thaku said, *"Calm down friends. All of you take your positions and close your eyes. I'll play the song that suits the occasion."*

As the tape was turned on, everybody was curious and excited. *"Which song could it be?"* Just then the voice came up. *"PUT ON THE MUSIC!*

[3.] Chiranjeevi – South Indian film star

START THE MUSIC!" The boys started dancing in elation. *"G A N G; GANG GANG bajao GANG GANG,"* shouted the boys. *"GANGLEADER!"*

The atmosphere turned jubilant as we went crazy dancing. The music boomed through the entire street. Surprised villagers stepped out of their homes. A few sauntered towards us, amusedly looking at a bunch of ecstatically dancing children.

All of a sudden, out of nowhere, Krishnaveni appeared. Pushing her way through the frenzied mob, she called out to me. I was in no mood to listen to her. She pulled me out of the crowd, by my arm. Once out of the crowd, she had my attention.

"What?"

"Come home immediately. It's important."

"No way. I want to dance."

She looked anxiously at me. *"I know you are on a musical high right now but I have got mind-blowing news for you."*

"Oh! is it? Sis, don't waste my time. What is it?"

"You have got a letter by post, my dear brother."

"Me? a letter? From where?"

"Guess!"

"Look! I have no time for guessing. I want to have fun. Look at my friends here. I am not coming with you. Please leave me. Let me dance."

"Stupid! The post is from Sainik School."

"What!!! Are you kidding!!! I can't believe it!!!"

We began running. As we neared our house I stopped. Turning to Krishnaveni with a serious face I asked, *"Are you conning me into having milk?"*

"No, not today! Don't be silly," she laughed. *"Look at the postman there.... standing inside, near the door."*

"Well, now you sound genuine, my dear sis," I smiled and raced towards the gate.

I have been waiting for this letter so badly and now it has come. Or has it not? One look at mother's face confirmed it all. Oh, I'd never felt happier! Punching my fist in the air I furiously rushed to hug my mother. Her eyes were tearful, but she was smiling. As tears rolled down her cheeks, I whispered, *"I won't go anywhere leaving you, mother."*

"Now, don't give lame excuses to stay and continue with your childish pranks here," a booming cheerful voice scolded. It was father. I beamed as I hugged him.

"Life is what you make out of it, and I know that you are capable of doing so much more, my son. Now get ready and go to take the blessings of our Lord."

My selection was a matter of pride not only for my family but also for my village – Kondrapole. I was the first student to achieve this merit. Sainik Schools are hailed as one of a kind schools in India.

English medium schools had begun spreading in rural India around 1990s. I was fortunate enough to be one of the first from our village to enroll in an English medium school. My elder siblings had done their schooling in the local vernacular Telugu medium, as there were no English medium schools when they began schooling. Admissions to Sainik School were open for students of both mediums. However, post-admission, English was the only medium of instruction.

Bowing down to my parents, I took their blessings and took a shower before visiting our temple with the admission letter. With joy and reverence, I placed the letter at the feet of Lord Sri Rama after applying tilak on my forehead and the letter.

"My Lord! Thank you! Thank you for today! Every day of my life is full of joy and happiness. Thank you! Now, I will be leaving for a school that is far away from here, don't ever desert me, my Lord. I am nothing by myself, yet I am everything when You are with me."

"Please take care of my family. Though I will not be able to come here, you will always be in my thoughts. I love you for everything you have blessed me with." I closed my eyes and knew that I would never be alone. Shri Rama would always be with me.

Picking up the letter I rushed back to my friends who were still dancing to the rhythm of the music.

"Heya Guys! I have made it to Sainik School." I was shouting myself hoarse and shaking my friends' shoulders but it didn't distract them from dancing. The blaring music kept all busy. I went to the tape recorder and shut it off.

"What?" I got the attention of two dozen agitated and vexed faces.

"Clam down friends. I have a huge announcement."

"What announcement? Are you getting married or what?" sneered Bala. *"How luccckyyy…"* teased Saida.

"No, you idiot, I have got admission to Class 6th at Sainik School. I'll be leaving shortly for school," I replied triumphantly.

"Why the hell do you want to join Sainik School leaving us all here?" An irritated Mahesh fumed. *"Wait let me explain."* I countered. *"First of all, it's not just any other school. It is Sainik School."*

"So what? Are they going to teach you from Z to A?" asked Thaku.

I smiled, *"I don't have to learn Z-A. In Grade 6, probably for people like you, they might do it that way."* There was laughter and someone chimed *"Yeah! He needs someone who teaches him that way."*

"What's so special about it? Why do you want to go to a new school anyway?"

"There isn't a single thing that is not special about this school," I explained, counting the list of stationery and uniform the school would provide me on joining. *"I will be getting a cricket bat, a hockey stick, football shoes, raincoat. There will be different uniforms for different activities". "That's crazy and unbelievable dude!"* they shouted.

"We have horse riding," I smiled.

"*That's unbelievable!!*" they yelled.

"*Not just that, there is a swimming pool too,*" I murmured in a low voice.

"*What? Those pools we see in movies where the heroines dive in wearing bikinis?*" The gang looked at me in astonishment and awe.

"*Of course,*" I grinned.

"*My wow! That's big!*"

"*Yes. We have seen all these only on television, but now I'm going to live it in real.*" I didn't mean to brag but was over the moon.

"*That's huge, man. Congratulations!*" My friends grabbed me for a tight hug.

"*So, let's rock on.*" Thaku turned on the stereo.

The notes of *BANGARU KODI PETTA* a song from the film *Gharana Mogudu* boomed through the hot humid breeze. The volume of the stereo again rose to our rising energy and boisterous enthusiasm. Villagers passing by, stood close and watched us for a while before walking away. We continued gyrating, leaping, and rollicking to the music with new dance moves.

The day to leave for school approached close. My family busied in preparing snacks for me. They were happy, proud, and worried. I would miss them terribly.

The night before my departure was a quiet one. Dinner was delicious, but silence reigned. "*Here - have some more chicken,*" offered my brother.

"*Your favorite dishes will remind us of you,*" sniffled my eldest sister.

"*How will you manage at the hostel?*" fretted my mother.

"*That's the only way he will learn to eat everything,*" father consoled her.

"*I hope so,*" sighed mother.

"*The school is at least twelve hours away. We can't even visit him when we want to.*" Mother's voice was slowly breaking into a sob. I stood quietly listening.

"I surely don't want to go now." The others looked at me bewildered. *"To leave all this for just a new school! I won't have anybody there who will be concerned about me like you Ma. I will be one among all unlike the only pampered one here."*

I implored father. *"At the new school, I won't have you, father, to gently coax me to do what I have to. Mother won't be there to prepare my favourite dishes. I will miss my siblings, my toys. I will miss my village, and all the fun with my friends. For what? At what cost?"*

"We will miss you too. Look, if you stay back, you will remain to be one among us. But if you go, you will be one among a crore!" encouraged my brother.

My father held my hand as he spoke very quietly. *"Rama, it is the right time to explore the outside world. As the Bhagavad-Gita says, 'The entire realm of action ends in wisdom'. We all have our part to play. Now go and play your best game. Do us all proud."*

"Don't even think of staying back my son. We all are born to learn and evolve. This is a great opportunity" added my mother; *"you see, you will be here for three months in a year, during the vacations. So, you will not miss any fun here either."*

The train was expected at 5 pm. My friends and neighbours kept turning up at my home during the day to wish and cheer me. The day flew in a flash.

I hugged my friends before I left for the railway station. My family had come to Miryalaguda, to see me off. On the platform, Sudhakar (Sudha), my cousin who lived in the neighbouring village, waited with his parents. He too had secured admission in Sainik School.

I was elated. Our families looked relieved.

"Boys, ensure that you write home regularly, okay? We will be waiting for your letters," smiled Sudha's father.

"Life changes in the blink of an eye. They will do well," stated my father. We were engrossed in chatting when the loudspeaker above made loud and strange noises. The announcer announced the arrival of the train. All of a sudden, the entire atmosphere turned somber and emotional.

It was about 7:00 pm when the train finally touched the platform. Our hearts beat faster. Our parents turned to prayer for the protection of their children. We took our parents' blessings as the train came chugging onto the platform and then rushed towards bogie S-6 lugging our black metal trunk boxes behind us.

Miryalaguda was a small station. Trains halted here for a mere two minutes. By the time we found our berths and arranged our luggage, the train began honking. We rushed to the windows to wave. Our families waved back; all smiles and tears. Slowly the blue-grey train picked up momentum, rolling through the greenery, taking us away from home, family and friends towards a new life. We leaned on each other as the train puffed out of the platform.

We reached Sainik School, the next morning by 9:00 am. It was a bright Sunday.

We walked through the entrance towards a counter. The lady there smiled a welcome. *"Ramakrishna and Sudhakar. You are on time."*

She instructed us to freshen up and stay in the Maurya House for time being and asked us to assemble at the administrative block by 3:00 pm post-lunch for further proceedings. We reached the house and saw about 20-25 boys jumping on their beds. One of the boys was walking in a circle around the room. Bare-chested with a towel around his neck he puffed his wiry chest as he walked. The towel was now on the floor. Holding a stick like a sword he faced me with a smug smile, *"I am Alexander-The Great."*

"Wow, now I can proudly say that Alexander-The Great is my friend," I smiled and hugged him. Alexander was all smiles.

"Well, I am Nihar."

"I am Ramakrishna."

The new admissions to class 6, scheduled to arrive by noon that day were directed to Maurya House. Most of the students seemed to know each other. They either studied at the same coaching centers or they had met during the admission interview. A good number of qualified students came from a popular coaching centre located not far away from the school campus.

We were delighted to meet Deepak (Deepu) – we studied at the same coaching center. Sudha looked around for more familiar faces. *"Kishore is on the waiting list,"* stated Deepak. Let's hope he makes it too.

By 3:00 pm we reached the administrative block. It was a majestic building with a towering arch. We were told that it used to be a Palace earlier.

A new batch of eager beavers was on the way to the administrative block. Two white elephants carved out of a single block of marble stood on either side of the entrance. A small crowd had gathered around the elephant. I made my way through. We eagerly waited for our turn to sit on the elephants. Barring a few, most of the students were from Andhra Pradesh. The whole group were now engaged in cheery chatter and seemed to love the place.

Suddenly out of nowhere came an old man riding a bicycle and stopped right near us. He was tall and athletic, clean-shaven, and wore glasses. He looked almost bald except for a wad of snowy white hair at the back. I kept looking at him taking in his crisp white uniform; his neatly tucked-in shirt and polished shoes.

"Come on children, all of you assemble here." No response.

Well, nobody knew him and at that moment the elephants were more important.

The old man seemed someone important. He didn't like being ignored. He had an image to maintain and children not paying attention to him didn't help one bit.

"Can't you hear me?" he hollered. *"Just come and assemble here."*

The anger and the loud voice had their effect. The boys began filing in one behind another. Happy that he was now regarded with interest and respect, he introduced himself as Mr. Rao, senior Master, and addressed the students.

"We welcome today, to Sainik School, the new batch of Grade 6. As per norms, class 6 students report to the school one week in advance for a crash program, to understand the routine. You might have seen that there are 8 houses in the school; of which four are senior houses and four junior houses."

"You will be allocated to the four junior houses based on your ranking, to ensure uniformity of merit among all the houses. Students from classes 6 to 8 will stay in junior houses and students from classes 10 to 12 in senior houses. Class 9 students are divided into both the junior and senior houses. Each junior house is connected to a senior house where they will move into, after they complete class 8 or 9, as per the discretion of their housemasters. The colour of the flaps you wear on your uniform mark your house."

The 4 junior houses	Maurya	Pallava	Pandya	Kakatiya
The 4 senior houses	Gajapati	Gupta	Chalukya	Moghul
House Colour	Red	Green	Yellow	Blue

"There will be separate inter-house competitions for junior and senior houses. They include sports, athletics, cross-country, indoor games, swimming, dramatics, academics. Debates, quizzes and extempore speech competitions will also carry points. Based on the performances for the current academic year the best among both the senior and junior houses will be declared as Cock Houses for the next academic year," explained Mr. Rao.

The school attendants stood ready with the school uniform and stationery.

Mr. Rao continued, "*You will be given a roll number for your academic career in this school. Even after you leave, you will be referred as a Saikorian with your roll number.*"

Those who became friends in that short period naturally wished to be together. The names were called out. Roll numbers were assigned. Houses were allocated. Slowly they moved towards the counter to receive their uniforms and material.

"*Oh Wow!!! A raincoat!*" someone pointed excitedly. "*That's pretty amazing. I've never worn one before,*" said the other.

"*Why are the socks so long?*" asked another.

"*They are stockings; you must double fold them while wearing,*" explained the attendant.

"*Ramakrishna, roll no. 3027. House Pallava.*"

"*Football shoes! Oh wow!*" I exclaimed. "*These shoes are so perfect!*" I couldn't believe it was happening.

"*We are not dreaming, right?*" I asked Sudha. Sudha smiled, "*Of course not.*"

"*Sudha, roll no. 3028. House Pandya.*"

Deepak was 2955 also a Pandyan. Allocation of houses and distribution of uniforms and accessories went on for two hours.

Mr. Rao was speaking, but it seemed pointless addressing a group of ecstatic boys, going through their new hoard with bright eyes. He was not sure if we were listening to him. "*Congratulations to all of you, for making it to Sainik School. This is going to be a great beginning and a huge foundation for your life. The next seven years will teach and equip you for life. Tomorrow onwards your day will commence with an early morning siren at 5:00 am. This is a mock drill so that you get acclimatized to the school routine. You may now disperse and move to your respective houses; will see you in action from tomorrow.*"

A loud and shrill siren rang through the houses at 5:00 the next morning. It was long and continuous. The new batch did not hear. They were dead asleep. The dormitory lights were turned on and a voice broke, *"wake up you idiots, it's time for your PT[4]."*

It didn't make any difference to sleeping boys who had slept late after a night of exciting incessant chatter.

The voice was now fierce. *"Get out of your beds; I am your housemaster here."*

Revanth jumped out of his bed saying, *"Sir, Sir."*

"Wake up all your friends immediately and get ready for PT." shouted the housemaster.

"Are you crazy Revanth? Why the hell are you waking us up?" an irked Bhuvan pulled back his sheet and covered his head.

"Kick you bloody fellow Bhuvan get up now" - shouted the housemaster. Bhuvan sat up astonished, but now fully awake.

"Now wake up everybody" shouted the housemaster and walked away. Within the next five minutes, everyone in the dormitory was awake, groaning and cribbing.

"Never in my life have I woken up so early," grumbled Suresh. *"As if I have!"* moaned Rajesh. *"It is only 5! I need to sleep."* I curled up sleepily and was turning to my side when Pradeep shook me again. *"Don't do that. Our housemaster is around."*

This was a feature in all the houses. Cursing the school curriculum and missing our homes, we dragged ourselves out.

"I just can't imagine living with this daily routine," stated G.S. Kalyan.

"I wish there was no PT," whined Harsha.

By 5:40 am, we, grade 6 of Pallava House stood ready, outside our house, all wearing bright white PT uniforms, waiting for our housemaster. The Housemaster Mr. Subayya arrived shortly and ordered us to fall-in 3s[5]

[4.] PT- Physical Training

[5.] 3's – rows of 3 each

according to our height. *"Remember to go this way for every activity without being asked,"* he added.

We reached the ground and were amazed by its vastness. The little 6th graders could see only flat land as far as they could see.

"This is insane, man!" exclaimed B. Kiran (B.K.). B.K. was lean and physically fit. He wasn't very tall.

"Huuuge indeed!!" repeated an equally awe-struck Suresh.

They turned around to the sound of a shrill whistle. It was the PT master, Mr. Reddy. *"Students, fall-in line house-wise."*

He took the roll-call. *"Now start running. Two tracks today."* Only after we began to run, did we realize how huge the track was. In a few minutes, we were drenched in perspiration. *"Who in the world wakes up at 5 to do PT? This is cruelty!"* cried G.S. Kalyan. *"Is this a school or a prison?"* wailed Srinivas.

After body-stretching exercises, we had to run another two tracks. We were deadbeat when the PT session ended.

B.K. remarked, *"I enjoyed this run, though it was annoying to wake up early in the morning."* We stared at him incredulously.

"Thank God, it's over!" said a tired Suresh.

"It's not time to thank God yet," said Rajesh sagely.

"Why?" enquired a concerned Suresh.

"Because we have it again tomorrow," yelled Rajesh. *"This is a routine, man!"* The group looked at Rajesh disbelievingly.

"Are you crazy? I don't think so. PT is once or twice a week," I opined.

"We will see tomorrow." An annoyed Rajesh walked towards the house.

We reached our house and saw a kettle kept outside. Ramu shouted out, *"Hey Guys, look! A milk kettle."* Ramu had topped the entrance exam and was regarded with respect. We rushed into our dormitory and queued near the kettle with our glass tumblers.

Suresh tilted the kettle to pour out milk. It turned out to be tea.

"Oh No!" Cried out Ramu. *"What do we do now? I never had tea before."*

"Even, I haven't," consoled Harsha. *"But we don't have a choice here. This is life at boarding school. To survive we need to get used to change."*

"Let's raise our first toast of tea friends," I raised my glass of tea.

"No Time Guys. We are late for classes," declared Harsha. *"Get ready quickly. It's 6:30 already. We have only 30 minutes."*

"Oh!!! There is no time to rest with this crazy schedule," complained Virat.

"We will wear our school uniform for the first time today," stated a cheery Pradeep.

"Oh Yeah! Let's get ready," I replied.

By 6:50 fully dressed in our uniforms, we stood preening before the only framed mirror on the wall. We were gloriously happy, wearing our khaki uniforms with the green shoulder flaps, belts, and stockings. Hair neatly combed, and faces shining with happiness.

A common thread of pride ran through all of us when we wore our uniforms. We had earned our uniform. At 6.55, we stood in a file, outside, waiting for the housemaster. He arrived. Started inspecting our shoes, nails, and hair and then nodded towards our class.

Our class had two sections; A and B; Deepu and I were in section A while Sudha was in B. The class looked colourful with students wearing red, green, yellow, and blue shoulder flaps.

Within minutes the class turned noisy. We bantered like we have known each other for ages. The English teacher entered the class quietly and greeted us, 'Good Morning Children.'

Nobody heard him.

"I am Anand, your English teacher," he said. The boys looked quizzically at him as if to ask, *So what? Who cares?*

Mr. Anand slapped himself twice and told, *"I am sorry. I am not able to control you, it's my failure."* The class went pin-drop silent.

"Is he crazy or what?" I murmured. Suresh nudged me. *"Shh!"*

The first two periods passed in no time. It was time for breakfast. The breakfast menu was fixed for the week. On Mondays, there was bread omelet for non-vegetarians and bread cutlet for vegetarians along with ketchup.

Cutlets were not normally prepared in South-Indian kitchens. The boys looked at it warily and had to be coaxed to eat. The non-vegetarians loved their omelets. Assembly was after breakfast.

Mondays were special. The entire school assembled in the auditorium and was addressed by the principal. On other days, we had three separate assemblies; first for class 6th and 7th together, second for 8th to 10th, and third for 11th and 12th at different venues. We had to hone our oratory skills. Each day was hosted by a house. Four boys from that house, would speak on a topic of choice for two minutes.

The bell rang at 9:40 for the third period and then after the fifth period we got a milk-break at 11:40. Two more periods after that at 1:20 pm, we broke for lunch. The classes went smoothly. We returned to our houses to put back our bags and went towards the mess.

"*I hope we get crisply fried ladyfinger, dal curry, and sambar with curd,*" wished Bhuvan. "*I hope we get fried potatoes*" hoped a hungry Harsha.

We rushed into the mess at lunch break.

"*What is it?*" I asked. "*I mean -for a curry.*"

"*You guys were wishing for fried food, here we are unable to even make out what curry this is!*" B.K. laughed.

"*I think it could be snake gourd,*" explained Manohar.

"*What? snake gourd? Oh no! This is terrible. I don't mind skipping lunch. I just can't eat snake gourd,*" replied Revanth.

"*Why skip lunch? Have rice with sambar,*" offered B.K.

"*That's even worse,*" whined Ramu. "*This watery liquid is called sambar here. And where is curd?*" asked Virat. "*There it is! Just stir it, it will turn to buttermilk,*" laughed G.S. Kalyan.

"What the hell!" cried Rajesh.

Just then Revanth took out a bottle from his pocket. *"What's that?"*

"PICKLE."

"Wow!"

Within no time, the bottle was empty. Revanth kept looking disbelievingly at the empty bottle. He couldn't complain. His friends were thanking him so joyfully.

"The problem doesn't end here guys, it's just the beginning" warned Pradeep. *"Let's see what's in store for us in the days to come, but for now, we can just thank Revanth,"* I said warily

"That's true," agreed everybody in unison. In just two days, I had impressed my housemates with my ability to spin fantastic stories at the drop of a hat.

Post-lunch we got some time to rest. It was storytime. I narrated stories with humor, emotion, inspiration, adventure, and drama. I spoke of ghosts, kings, and ancient lore. Very soon I was popular. As I was often surrounded by a ring of friends, gathered to hear my stories, our housemaster had named me **Ring Leader Ramakrishna.** Though I bonded with all, I had a relaxed closeness with- Harsha, Suresh, Rajesh, B. Kiran, Karthik, Pradeep, and G.S. Kalyan. I spent time with them but missed my coaching center friend, Kishore who was still on the waiting list.

Self-Study hour was from 3:15-4:15 pm for completing our lessons and assignments. We were required to wear our sports uniforms. Our sport-shirts had the house colour. We wore white shorts and canvas shoes. Our eyes kept moving to the large clock in the room. Our games time was from 4:30 to 5:30 pm. We were eagerly waiting for **FOOTBALL**.

The ground seemed warm and bright now. We felt energetic and enthusiastic, very different from the morning. It was vast - about fifty acres.

"Guess what? There are bloody twelve FOOTBALL COURTs in toto, dude. Isn't it crazy?" detailed B.K. *"and not just football courts; there are two*

basketball courts, three volleyball courts, two handball courts, one hockey court, and a cricket ground" added Revanth.

"You have perfect information on everything; hats off to you Revanth" complemented Suresh.

The shrill whistle sounded to disperse and play. We had never played on such a huge ground with a football in real. We enjoyed the game thoroughly and almost didn't hear the closing whistle. We looked dejected at each other - the sports period had ended too soon.

Everybody was perspiring, except me.

"Just look at you," exclaimed B.K. *"You are as thin as a feather and you don't perspire!* I smiled; *you will find my shirt wet only when it rains."*

We stepped back into our house, to find the kettle waiting. *"Ramu, there is MILK just for you; for others there is tea,"* I offered as Ramu grinned.

We were only beginning to get used to drinking tea; some of us had even begun liking it. *"Make it fast boys, its 5:40 pm already, you need to be in the study hall by 6:00 pm,"* warned our housemaster.

By 6:00 pm all of us were in the study hall dressed in white trousers, full-sleeved shirts, and ties. The clock was slowly ticking towards 8:00 pm. Our faces turned sour just thinking of dinner.

"I don't even want to come for dinner," declared Vamsi.

"Me too," agreed Bhuvan.

"We have no choice; we have to report for dinner," countered, Suresh.

After the roll-call was over, we entered the mess in trepidation.

"Did anybody bring some pickles?" asked Revanth. *"Don't, worry I did,"* I patted my trouser pocket as we walked inside.

It was chicken for the non-vegeterians and paneer curry for the veggies. We were pleasantly surprised and happy.

"Can you believe it?" asked a surprised Vamsi.

"It's real dude. You don't have to doubt it," replied Pradeep.

Overhearing our conversation, the attendant explained – "*Boys, the equation is simple here. It all starts with breakfast. If you have a good breakfast in the morning, it is followed by a disaster lunch and a good dinner and likewise. It's all about balance. Don't worry, your health will be taken care of. Now don't think or worry too much about food, instead enjoy whatever is served.*" He left laughing.

After a long day and a good dinner, we were tired and sleepy. We waited for the siren to end our day; but before that, we had to study for an hour – from 9:00-10:00 pm.

This was a real testing time as we nodded to sleep, some of us leaning on each other. At 10:00 pm, the siren went off. Few heard it. As most of us were in deep sleep and had to be shaken awake to go back to our dormitories.

The youngest batch lived this routine for the entire week. We had to get used to it before our seniors returned from their summer vacations. In time, we got used to the schedule and each other. We had forged a bond strong enough to last for the rest of our schooling or maybe for a lifetime.

When the week ended, the school administration arranged for a small cultural program for us. We participated enthusiastically by singing, dancing, mono-acts, and all that we knew. We cheered each other; the result was fantastic.

The faculty was pleased to see the new vibrant batch, but were concered about how we would adopt to the schedule and the life around us. They knew the next few days were going to play a crucial role in making or breaking our personalities.

The seniors would join school the day after the cultural program. The staff warned us to take care of ourselves and not to hesitate in approaching them in case of any trouble from our seniors. None of us lent our ears to the staff as we were all absorbed in the delicious food that was being served. Little did we know that it would be our only night of peaceful sleep for the next five years!

Chapter **2**	**Class VI**
	Part I – Arrival of the Seniors

The day began lazily. It was serene and calm. A Sunday. We had been to the mess for breakfast. I was returning to the house lobby with a few of my classmates. The seniors who had just arrived, stood watching us. We greeted them and introduced ourselves.

"*Welcome to Sainik School,*" offered the tallest of them. They looked like 9th graders.

"*So how was your crash program,*" enquired another with a smirk.

"*It was fun, memorable. We were looking forward to meeting you,*" I replied.

"*That's quite interesting,*" rejoined the tall boy. "*Have class 7th briefed you on the rules?*"

"*Not yet! But we know them. We were briefed during the crash program.*"

"*Is that so!!! Where are the 7th graders?*" he hollered.

A boy came running. Tall, lanky, expressionless.

He stood facing him. "*Yes, Master.*"

"Well, Paparayudu," he looked at the 7ᵗʰ grader. *"It seems the 6ᵗʰ graders already know the rules of the school. Were you too, a part of their crash program?"*

"No Master. We have just arrived. We undeniably apologize for not addressing them so far. I will instruct them right away."

"Better do it immediately. Else, you will have to report to me."

Paparayudu looked worried as he nodded his head and let out a deep breath as he left.

"What's your name?"

"I'm Ramakrishna."

"Call your batchmates."

As we gathered, he began commanding, *"Forget all the rules you've learned so far. You will obey our rules."*

"The seniors are on their way. They arrive in batches, by different trains. So far only the first batch has arrived. By noon, everybody will be here."

The tall boy left. Looking towards him, Paparayudu continued – *"That was Rupesh. He is the Master. One of your Masters."* His voice was commanding now.

"The foremost rule is, whenever seniors call you, go running."

"Address them as Master."

"Never look into their eyes. Never."

"When you sight your seniors being punished, bow your head."

"Never say 'No' to your seniors. Don't even think of it."

"If they punish you, bear it quietly."

'Don't ever dare question them. They have their reasons."

"Be vigilant. If you are inattentive and don't hear their call by mistake, pray to God for your safety."

"When asked to kneel, don't just kneel. Jump in the air and then land on your knees."

"What if we don't land on our knees?" I wondered loudly.

"*Simple. You will keep kneeling till you land perfectly, and, in the process, you might end up getting slapped midair,*" laughed Paparayudu.

"*So, we should land straight on the knees in the very first attempt,*" I murmured.

"*How can they be so inhumane?*" lamented Bhuvan.

"*Can't we report to our housemaster?*" asked Vamsi in a conspiratory voice.

Paparayudu heard, He gave a sarcastic smile. "*Whom would you report to? Bampu???*"

"*Bampu!!!! Who is he?*" asked Revanth.

"*Oh! I forgot to tell you. With all due respect, we call our housemaster 'Bampu',*" sneered Paparayudu. "*The craft instructor is Tokada and the senior master – Mr. Rao is Kaddi (pole like). You will soon get used to these names.*"

"*Oh, God! Don't, we have any recourse to this bullying?*" blustered Ramu. "*Where have we landed? Have we slogged the entrance exam and interview for this?*"

Seeing the angry and bewildered faces around him, Paparayudu smiled. "*Know that your seniors including me have reached here through the same selection process. Remember we the class of 7, have been through class 6 like you. Don't worry guys, you will get used to it.*"

Paparayudu continued briefing us.

"*Each house has two dormitories; one is a senior's dormitory and the other is a junior's dormitory.*"

"*Students from classes 6 and 7 in junior houses and classes 9 and 10 in senior houses are accommodated in junior dormitories.*"

"*Students from classes 8 and 9 in junior houses and classes 11 and 12 in senior houses are accommodated in senior dormitories.*"

Paparayudu briefed us about ten more minutes after which he left; probably convinced that he had scared us enough to dominate us. *Such a Bully he was!* His voice still rang inside our heads. We looked around the quarters, walking close to each other for comfort. Touring the place now was pointless. The houses and the lobbies looked similar.

The dormitories were rectangular. A path from the entrance ran in-between the dormitory, right to the end, where the washrooms were.

The houses had beautiful gardens in the front, through which passed the main entrance. The housemasters lived near the entrance. Their quarters were to the left. Towards the right was the recreation room. After that came the storeroom to the left and study hall to the right.

The open space in between the study hall and the juniors' dormitory was often used for playing cricket. The space between the storeroom and the seniors' dormitory had a flowerbed. The juniors' dormitory was next to the emergency water tank near which there was open space for brushing and washing shoes.

The open space next to the seniors' dormitory was the KABADDI COURT. It was a witness to casualties of every junior Saikorian in both the houses. On either side were four separate washrooms for seniors and juniors.

Only the house captains in the junior house had the authority to punish a class 8 student. The same wasn't practiced in the senior houses as there was no tradition of seniority for immediate batches.

Both the house captain and vice-captain were from class 9 in junior houses. Whereas in senior houses, house captains were from class 12 and the vice-captains were from class 11. So, class 8 guys were the most privileged in the junior houses.

After all the seniors of Pallava house arrived, the Housemaster Bampu ordered class 9th boys to report to him. The air was tense; he was announcing names of boys who would move to the Gupta house. The students had a stony expression as their names were called out. Their friends bid them a warm farewell as they shifted to the Gupta house.

On the same day, a few new 9th graders joined the school. The school took new admissions in class 6 and class 9. Annually about 70 students join in grade 6 and 20 join grade 9th. The new joinees to the 9th-grade were accomodated in junior houses only. Though they join directly in class 9, their situation is no better than class 6 boys - at times is even worse. Their experience as a Saikorian is considered equal to that of class 6 students. Even class 6 guys are deemed senior to them by a week by virtue of their crash program. They don't get treated at par by the juniors or even by their own classmates. So, it was tougher for them to get used to the school than the class 6 guys. The worst was that their own classmates treated them as outsiders. There were very few exceptions to this.

The next day we had a special assembly. It was for welcoming the new students of classes 6 and 9, announcing the COCK HOUSE – the Champion Houses and the new appointments for the year.

Maurya House among the junior houses and Moghul house among the senior houses stood as the Cock Houses. We had captains for all activities - school captain, school adjutant, games captain, mess captain, cultural captain, and all their vice-captains. We also had class monitors. Newly appointed captains were presented with different shoulder flaps to distinguish their designation. The entire auditorium was jubilant with thundering applause for all the new captains. Both Maurya and Moghul houses were over the moon celebrating their championship. Cadet Ravindranath was appointed as school captain, Gagan Pawan as house captain, Harish as the vice-captain of Pallava house, and Baji Babu as the Class-Prefect for A Section of Class 6.

After the event, the new captains of Pallava house asked us to fall-in, inside the kabaddi court post-lunch. During the fall-in, we had a brief introductory session. They instructed the rules of the school system and the results of deviations. They also advised us to report to them in case of any problems.

During our briefing, Mohan a 7th class guy was heard speaking in Telugu[6] with Mukesh. Gagan hollered, *"Come here both of you."* They came running. Gagan ordered them to kneel, and they kneeled to perfection landing on their knees. Nobody from our class had any clue about what was happening and why they were being punished.

"What made you speak in Telugu?" fumed Gagan.

"Master since the Token isn't introduced yet; we took the liberty to speak in Telugu."

A loud slap landed on Mukesh's face. Harish stood a foot away from him; his right hand still in air.

"Do you guys expect to be informed officially every year about the Token system?

"Sorry Master. Sorry," cowered Mukesh in fear.

"I will not repeat it, Master."

"Mohan, do you expect us to officially introduce it for class 7 now?" bellowed Gagan.

"No Master no, certainly not!" Mohan's voice was close to a sob.

"Now get lost from here," barked Harish.

Mukesh and Mohan vanished in no time.

Hearing the commotion, the newly appointed captains turned towards the new 6 graders. Two frightened boys looked at them in mute appeal.

"Don't panic," smiled the captains. *"As you get used to the rules, it will become a part of your routine."*

---

6. Telugu- Regional language of AndhraPradesh, India

"I think you guys must have been briefed about what is expected out of you by class 7th boys," interjected Harish.

"Yes, Master" shouted the class 6 students. *"Good"* replied Gagan.

"What did you learn from what happened just now?"

"Master we should not speak in Telugu" offered Bhuvan.

"Good. You are quick learners. First, understand the process. A Token (a small piece of wood over which TOKEN is inscribed) will be given to you if you are caught speaking in Telugu. Whosoever has the Token with them after lunch and after dinner will have to report to either of us for speaking in Telugu. Is this understood?"

"Yes, Master!"

"Of course, you have just seen what happens to the one who holds the Token," smiled Gagan.

We went blank hearing this.

"Well then. Welcome to Sainik School. It's going to be the best journey of your life. Learn the process. You will survive. If you learn to survive here, you can survive anywhere under any circumstances. Don't panic or become homesick. Adapt to this life for another five years starting today. You may disperse now," they commanded.

We walked back to our dormitory. Each of us was given a bed with an attached window and a cupboard. The entire dormitory had beds and cupboards arranged alternately.

The scene of the Token and the punishing slaps stayed with us the entire evening. Our hearts sank in fear. We were aware of the bullying and were unable to do anything now. During the Crash course, we had bonded well. We had an unspoken tactical understanding between two or three groups (like the power blocks post World War II) that we would not pass on the Token among ourselves. It was like an informal peace treaty on not exchanging the Token within the group. It meant that the left-outs would be targeted. My team and I took the Token and spoke freely in Telugu till lunchtime. Only team members knew who is holding the Token. Meanwhile, we manipulated Bhuvan to speak in Telugu just before the reporting time.

Poor chap, though he managed to keep away from the Token throughout the day, he was purposely needled by Rajesh and compelled to use the word AMMA which meant 'mother' in Telugu. The moment he uttered it; he was given the Token by Rajesh.

Poor Bhuvan began crying, *"you can't pass on the Token for using the word AMMA; it is a word we often use."* But the majority supported Rajesh and Bhuvan was given the Token forcefully.

Seeing Bhuvan in distress, I volunteered to take the Token from him. I concurred, *"don't worry Bhuvan, I'll take the Token from you"* to an astounded Bhuvan.

"Are you crazy? You have seen the fate of the 7th grader. Why do you want to willfully invite the same fate?" demanded a surprised Rajesh.

As Bhuvan looked on, I explained, *"It's our Bhuvan after all. Let me see what they are going to do."* Nobody said anything. They scratched their head and wondered why I was doing this. When lunch break got over, I headed towards the senior dormitory.

Bhuvan stopped me. *"Let me go Rama."*

"May be another time" I replied and ran up to Gagan's bed.

I went and stood by Gagan's bed. Joel of class 9 asked, *"why are you here?"*

"I have the Token."

"So, you are the first causality," laughed Joel, as Gagan entered the dormitory.

I stood there. Waiting.

"What brings you here," asked Gagan.

"Token, Master."

Gagan smiled and asked, *"What did you speak in Telugu?"*

"I didn't Master, Bhuvan spoke."

"What? Come again."

"I didn't speak in Telugu, it's Bhuvan who got the Token and I took it from him."

"How dare you do that! Don't you know what you are going to get out of it?"

I replied – *"I do, Master"*

"What's your name?"

"I'm Ramakrishna."

Gagan took a bite of the RAMBO chocolate bar he was holding and announced, *"No, you are not Ramakrishna, you are RAMBO, now onwards."*

I was amazed and replied, *"Thank You, Master."*

Gagan patted my back and replied, *"you may leave now. But don't repeat this. If you do, that will be your last day. Now get the hell out of here."*

I ran back to my dormitory.

As I reached my bed, everybody came rushing to me.

I smiled; *"Yes, Master Gagan did give me."*

"Oh, God! I'm so sorry," said an apologetic Bhuvan.

"Don't say sorry Bhuvan."

"What?"

"No! Because of you, I have become RAMBO." I narrated what happened.

That's marvelous they exclaimed hugging me – *"Rama is now The Rambo."*

RamMohan, a tall and dark, athletic looking boy of class 8 was in-charge of gardening. He was supposed to get the gardening done by two class 6 boys on a daily basis. He had arranged us to come in for duty as per our roll numbers, in succession. Post-gardening, the workers for the day would report to him after which he inspected if the plants were watered well.

Kalyan and I shared gardening duty the next day. We contrasted each other. Kalyan was podgy and I was reed-thin. He was tall and I was short. He sat on the last bench, and I had to sit right on the first bench. I was known for my wit and Kalyan was laid-back.

RamMohan was never satisfied with our gardening work. He always threatened "*I'm going to bash you, idiots. Do it again.*"

We were clueless as to why RamMohan was never happy with us. Whenever our turn came, we had to inadvertently hear from RamMohan, "*I am going to bash you, idiots. Do it again.*" We ended up with gardening duty for two or three days instead of one day, unlike the others.

My friend from coaching class Kishore had joined the school late and was now with me in the Pallava House. We were overjoyed. Kishore was also witty, and we enjoyed each other's company. Since Kishore had joined the school late by 45 days; he had to put in more study time to complete pending notes. I used to cue Kishore in on the unwritten rules and nuances of interacting with seniors.

For any activity, we had to fall-in files of three - like in NCC. It was normal for the house captain to say STOP any time. It happened at times, that the boys in the first file did not hear the house captains' order to STOP. They had to pay a huge price for it.

There was always a scramble to escape from the first file. Bhuvan – the bomber, and Revanth – the Kutchu; named after a similar character (in our textbook) who searched for his glasses though he had worn them, were confirmed to be the first two shortest guys of the class. Now the tussle for the second file was between Ramu (called Drum for his round body) and me. I won by popularity and filed into the second row.

The swimming pool was locked that year. I learned that during the previous year Mallesh, a new student of 9th grade had died accidentally inside the pool. I was a natural at telling stories. I whispered to my friends that Mallesh's ghost now haunts the swimming pool. My friends listened wide-eyed. They gathered near my bed post-lunch, during rest period, to listen to my blood-curdling, horror stories. Bampu was taking rounds to check whether we are resting. *"Kick you, bloody fellow ringleader Ramakrishna,"* he growled, *"you don't sleep and don't even let others sleep."*

I replied, *"Sir it's the other way round Sir, they won't sleep and don't let me sleep."*

"You bloody fool," he muttered before walking away.

It was a Sunday. Just before lunch, I was regaling my friends with a ghost story as usual, in which the protagonist Ravindranath (the school captain) was being chased by the ghost. Everybody around my bed was listening intently. The atmosphere was thick and silent with fear.

Right when all my audience were in jitters, we heard a long loud wail, *"Baabuuuu!"*

Everyone jumped and looked in the direction of the sound. The boys were trembling with fear and anxiety. With bated breath, they slowly looked out of the window to find Oil Raja looking inside. Everybody in a single voice shouted, *"you arsehole."*

Raja was popular as Oil Raja - a vagrant who only asks for hair oil. Nobody knew why he begged for oil.

Our housemaster came running hearing the racket. One of the guys from our class exclaimed *"Guys, look out Bampu is coming."* Unfortunately, this was overheard by the housemaster. But fortunately, he couldn't make out who said this. So, he walked away quietly.

He was full of anguish and emotional hurt as he walked back. He couldn't understand how the class 6 guys who have joined the school hardly a couple of months ago called him *Bampu*? He just couldn't take it. The name now haunted him. He didn't know how to respond but couldn't take action without knowing the culprit.

None of us sitting in that group realized that he overheard us calling him Bampu. We continued with the story. For lunch, the entire house filed and began moving towards the mess. The housemaster came out of his quarters and ordered the grade 6 boys to stay back.

All other boys of the house moved on to the mess. We had no clue, why we were asked to stay back?

Chapter **3**	# Class VI # Part II – Ignorant Mistakes

We were puzzled. Bampu had ordered only us to stay back. No one had a clue. Left to ourselves we began speculating. We watched Bampu as he walked towards us. Asking us to meet him in his office, he walked off briskly. All our speculations, assumptions, and jokes turned on their heads once we realized that there is a serious issue. We nervously entered his office room. He was sitting in his comfy chair with his head resting backward. On seeing us he tilted his head and quietly asked, *"who is Bampu?"*

Some of us squealed with laughter, some controlled. The smart ones looked at him surreptitiously. We had a strong suspicion that the conversation is leading us to disaster. In another minute the ones who were wildly laughing stopped sensing the terseness around. We waited, with bated breath, and heads bowed, waiting for the other shoe to fall.

The housemaster had begun probing.

"Is our principal the Bampu?"

"No Sir."

"Is our headmaster the Bampu?"

"No Sir."

"Ok. Is senior Master the Bampu?"

"No Sir."

Then he asked, *"Hey Bhuvan are you the Bampu?"*

Some of us again giggled.

"No Sir, I'm the Bomber, not Bampu."

"Who is the Bampu then?"

Silence

Finally, he asked. *"Is your housemaster the Bampu?"*

"Yes Sir," replied Vamshi spontaneously.

We were stunned and turned to stare at him in shock. Vamshi had blurted out of excitement. He hadn't paid it a thought and had got carried away by the bonhomie.

Vamshi realized what he had uttered as he felt the air around him freeze. The boys looked pointed daggers at him. We now had no choice but to collectively face the consequences.

Bampu was calm. He didn't seem to be in a hurry to bash us up.

"Who told you that your housemaster is Bampu?"

"Paparayudu," blurted Vamshi.

The tall boy who accosted us on our first day at school –Paparayudu tucked his shirts really neat and had a sinister expression all day.

"Alright then, you may leave now," snorted Bampu.

We were not punished. Relief and calm took place of anxiety. Relieved and happy we walked towards our mess, tagging a nagging thought that something had gone very very wrong.

Our mates from classes 7 to 9 were waiting for us for the roll-call outside the mess. We were exhausted running 500 meters from the house to the mess. All eight houses fell in for headcount before any activity. The entrance to the mess divided the junior houses from the senior houses. On to the left of the entrance were the junior houses and, on the right, stood the senior houses.

The mess hall was vast. It accommodated 600 students at a time. The houses had designated space. Discipline worked silently. Mischief lurked around. We had a secret parallel food distribution chain, running purely on barter. Food in exchange for food. A favorite snack, a bar of sweets, or pickles changed hands covertly.

We joined the Pallava house. A group of 7th graders pounced on us. *"What happened? Why did Bampu stop you? What did he say?"*

Suresh explained *"Boss[7]. Bampu's question was straight and to the point."*

"What was it?" Paparayudu was curious.

Suresh laughed aloud. *"He asked who is Bampu?"*

Paparayudu chortled loud and declared *"That Bampu has absolutely no common sense. Anyways what did you guys say?"*

Virat smirked, *"Our Vamshi said that our housemaster is Bampu."* Paparayudu burst out in laughter, *"Has he gone crazy? Why did he say that?"*

"You better ask him what happened next," mumbled Suresh.

"Hey man, Vamshi," admonished Paparayudu, *"why did you reveal that he was Bampu?"*

"Sorry Boss, I just said…. just that."

"What did you do?"

Vamshi explained, *"I messed up totally. After I admitted that our housemaster is Bampu, he asked me who told you that your housemaster is Bampu?"*

[7.] Boss - a slang used by those who shared warm relationships

"*What did you say then?*" Paparayudu was beginning to perspire.

"*I'm sorry. Please don't mind, Boss.*"

"*You idiot, first tell me whose name did you take?*"

"*Yours*".

"*You bastard Vamshi,*" exploded Paparayudu. "*When did I tell you that?*"

"*During our first interaction Boss,*" reminded Vamshi.

"*Oh, God! Do you realize what you have done? You have just booked me. Am I the only one who calls him Bampu? The entire school calls him by that name and you idiot have unnecessarily gotten me into this crap.*"

We were seated for lunch. Together. In a huddle. Chairs very close. Shoulders crouched. Heads together. Anyone could sense the nervousness. We didn't even see Bampu walk to our table. He was quietly sitting on a chair next to us.

The mess had separate dining spaces for teachers. The scandal of the day spread like wildfire. Paparayudu couldn't eat. He quietly gave away his food. It would be traded for food some other day. Fear and rage were building like a volcano within him. He felt helpless. Bampu's eyes bored into him. A shiver ran his spine. Paparayudu couldn't move. The bell rang. Lunch break was over. Paparayudu looked vulnerable today. I felt sorry for him.

We raced back to our dorms. The boys crowded around my bed for another story. I began spinning a new tale.

Intriguing and scary.

Like our day today.

The Housemaster Bampu strode into our dormitory. He had changed into a lungi[8] and was holding a bamboo cane in his hand. Walking briskly

---

[8.] Lungi- a cloth like a sarong, worn by men around the waist.

towards class 7 beds. The beds of sixth-graders were arranged near the entrance followed by the seventh graders' beds. As he walked towards the 7th class beds, Paparayudu went pale.

"Paparayudu looks really scared," expressed Suresh. I smiled saying, *"The thought of his pressed shirt getting crumpled must be more devastating to him."*

"Vamshi, lookout - Bampu is coming," warned Kalyan.

Bampu heard that. He Stopped. Fiercely looked at Kalyan. Cane in hand.

Kalyan was caned in mad anger. Bampu didn't heed to cries or pleadings today.

Bampu had initially forgiven 6th graders. He deemed that since we were new to the school his nickname could not be our idea. He had decided to teach the 7th graders a lesson. Kalyan was just plain unlucky. Paparayudu was spared.

Bampu stopped caning. He was looking at the cane. It was broken.

He stepped out of the dormitory yelling at them, *"You rascals, I won't spare you."*

Paparayudu hadn't stopped thanking his Gods and Kalyan.

Saved. Escaped by a whisker.

Kalyan was battered. He couldn't stand straight. We wanted to ease his pain, but he couldn't hear anything. All he saw, heard, and felt was pain. To add to his misery, it was his turn to do gardening that evening. I was his partner.

Kalyan and I walked to the garden to begin our work. I badly wanted to see him smile.

I asked. *"Hey Kalyan, who's the best in class 8? Why?"*

"Mahendra" (Mahi)- replied Kalyan. Mahi was a smart, intelligent, and good-looking guy. He was good at academics and games.

"No."

"Then who?"

"Its RamMohan."

"RamMohan!!! But why?"

"Since the day we have started gardening, how many times do you think he has warned us saying, 'I'm going to bash you, idiots. Do your work again."

"As many times as, we have done gardening."

"But did he ever bash us?"

"No," replied Kalyan.

"Then, isn't he the best?"

"That's a revelation dude," agreed Kalyan. *"I never thought of this."*

Just that moment RamMohan arrived for inspection and threatened, *"I'm going to bash you, idiots. Do it again."*

"Yes, Master," we replied rolling our eyes at each other.

As soon as he left, we just rolled there guffawing.

This time Kalyan didn't share this gag with anyone as he was still smarting from Bampu's beating.

However, I couldn't contain my excitement. It was my new, shiny, and rib-tickling joke. As our group walked to the ground for games, I posed this crack to my coaching center buddy Kishore and Rajesh, just for laughs. Very soon this joke spread and RamMohan became the hoot of the Pallava house.

While going through a blustery painful time, we used this as a joke to laugh and cool off.

As days passed, this joke reached the seniors; the class 7 boys. Though they found it funny they had a strong affinity with class 8 as well. Moreover, Paparayudu of Grade 7 wanted to use it to get even with the class 6 guys for putting him in a sticky situation with Bampu. So, he informed RamMohan, though he didn't know that the joke started from me. RamMohan felt angry and insulted.

The issue had become a matter of prestige for Class 8. They were infuriated. RamMohan along with his friends Ravinder, Srinivasulu, and Mahendra decided to teach the 6th graders a lesson.

We were oblivious to the grey storm that was brewing.

As the clock ticked towards 10:00, we waited for the siren to end our day. RamMohan and co. were waiting like a pack of wolves to pounce on them. Little did Kishore and Vamshi knew that. They were busy finishing their homework.

The seniors waited patiently for the 9th graders to leave the study hall, their eyes on Vamshi all the time.

It was 10:45. Only Kishore and Vamshi were left in the hall.

RamMohan and a few of his friends walked up to Vamshi. *"Hey Vamshi."*

Vamshi looked up from the book.

"Who is the best guy in class 8 and why?"

Vamshi understood where the conversation was heading. *"No Master, I don't know."*

RamMohan smiled. *"I heard that I am the best in class 8."*

"I'm the best. Right, Vamshi?"

RamMohan was standing very close now.

Vamshi was frightened. He looked around. The hall had only 8th graders. Some stood near him. Others began moving closer. He was clearly cornered. He didn't know how to respond.

"So, who started this joke? And who are the active propagators?" queried Ravinder.

"Vamshi, answer quickly or you will get it." Srinivasulu's voice was menacing.

Vamshi's heart was pounding hard. He realized he had no choice now.

RamMohan quietly offered, *"Look Vamshi, I will give you an option. If you give us the name, I'll make you my cadet⁹"* and ensure that you will be safe.

Vamshi was perspiring now. *"Ok Boss."*

"Well, That's like my cadet. Go on," encouraged RamMohan.

"Rambo started it, Boss" revealed Vamshi.

"It was propagated by Kishore and Rajesh. I have got nothing to do with it, Master. I never made any comment. Please spare me."

"You are my cadet now, so as promised, you will be left unharmed," assured RamMohan.

"Thank you, Master," replied a relieved Vamshi.

He looked at Kishore and shouted, *"Come here, you bastard."*

"Yes, Master!" Kishore was clearly flustered.

"So, I am the nicest guy from class 8, who never bashed you after saying - I will bash you, idiots. Isn't it, Kishore?" shouted RamMohan.

Even before Kishore could say anything a lightning slap landed on this cheek.

Kishore's eyes blurred with tears.

"You arshole, how dare you make fun of class 8. Kneel!" shouted RamMohan. As he leaped, Ravinder slapped him in midair. Kishore fell flat on the floor. The blow was hard and painful.

He cried aloud. *"Sorry Master, sorry. Please forgive me. I will never ever repeat it."*

"It's for what you did. Don't bother imagining what will happen to you if you even imagine repeating," warned Mahendra.

---

⁹. Cadet - A selected candidate under his protection

"Sorry Master, sorry!" replied Kishore.

"You bloody fuckers; you haven't tasted the medicine yet. If we ever get any sort of complaint, you know what could happen to you."

Kishore was crying and begging for forgiveness. *"Please Master I'm sorry."*

Looking at Kishore's state, the boys felt they have given a fair warning. *"Ask Rambo and Rajesh to report here tomorrow after dismissal."*

"Ok Master. Ok."

Kishore rushed to the dormitory still in tears. Entering the dormitory, he shouted *"You bloody bastard Rambo. Fuck you man, fuck you."* Everybody was fast asleep.

I woke up rubbing my smarting butt and looked up to see a furiously crying Kishore.

"What happened dude, what happened? Why are you crying?"

He kicked me again and again in anger.

He screamed *"this happened because I engaged in your joke on RamMohan."*

"Oh, God! What did he do? Are you coming from study hall now? I told you not to sit late there."

Hearing to the commotion, Rajesh woke up and joined us. *"What happened?"*

Kishore turned to him. *"It will be your turn tomorrow."*

"What are you saying?"

"Yes, RamMohan and his circle have asked both of you to report, post dispersal tomorrow." Rajesh and I couldn't sleep that night.

The next morning, as the siren for PT went off, we began feeling anxious.

I don't remember laughing since last night. Our jokes had brought us a nightmare. We were worried sick by afternoon thinking of our status post the dispersal siren. Past and future are only for reference, everything happens in the now.

The big clock in the Mess Hall seemed to tick fast. Its hands seemed to race today. We could eat nothing and gave away our food.

Post-lunch we didn't go straight to the dormitory thinking of ways to escape the impending doom. "*Let's pretend sick, we can rest in the Sick Bay,*" suggested Rajesh.

"*No, let's face him and get it over with,*" I suggested.

Rajesh agreed.

The day passed in superficial bravado.

After strolling around we reached our house by 3 pm and found that all our classmates looked perplexed.

"*Now what?*" I enquired.

"*Do you know What's happening in the Kabaddi court,*" exclaimed Suresh?

"*What?*"

"*Ask Kishore,*" replied Suresh.

"*Class 8 guys are being bashed by our House Prefects.*"

"*What for?*" I asked

"*For what they did to me last night,*" explained Kishore.

"*Oh my God! Did you report to our house captain?*"

"*No!*" replied Kishore.

Then how do they know?

Post-lunch I met my brother in Pandya house who is in class 9. He enquired on seeing my pale face, I told him about the previous night's happenings. "*My brother must have informed our captains.*"

"*You ass! You have unnecessarily made a mess out of it now; they are going to screw us for sure*"! exploded Rajesh.

"*So, what do we do? Should we report to them or just keep quiet?*"

"*It's really messed up now,*" murmured Rajesh.

"*Let's report to them as if we are not aware of all this,* I suggested. *Let's see how they respond.*"

As we walked towards the ground for games, we overheard class 7 boys talking, "*I think these class 6 guys are going against the tide. It might turn difficult to handle, later on,*" opined Paparayudu.

Rajesh and I looked at each other and continued walking. "*It is just a matter of time Rama; one day very soon we will be the bosses...*" Rajesh trailed off.

It was sports hour. We were playing football. I normally played as a forward. But today I slowly took center back position so that I could speak to Rajesh who was the keeper today. Kalyan joined me. The situation was grim and the only thing we could do was to laugh it off saying, "*Let's get our butt kicked.*"

The time for reporting was getting close. As the siren time for dispersal neared, we began praying to God for help.

The siren rang. The study hall was almost empty. Rajesh and I sat close. Holding hands. Waiting.

When the mind is in fear, we die a thousand deaths before we actually die.

By 10:35, the hall was empty except for Rajesh, me, RamMohan, and his friends from class 8. We mustered courage and walked up to RamMohan.

"*Master, Kishore has asked us to report to you.*"

"*You tiny little bastards, we know your game. Don't play too smart. We are completing this academic year in a couple of months. So, enjoy yourselves for the time being.*"

"*We will be waiting for you next year. Remember that. You will be in grade 7 and we will be in 9 and all the Prefects will be from our batch.*"

"*So Good night and GOOD LUCK to you guys - for the next academic year.*"

For the next one week, we the 6th graders of Pallava house were demotivated and lived in fear. Slowly as we got into a routine, we became cautious of what we spoke, when we spoke, to whom we spoke, and where we spoke. We became tight-lipped in common areas and were ourselves only inside our classrooms.

Our classrooms became more of complaining rooms. The discussion focused on new limits of wickedness and cruelty.

Had there been a debate among the 6th graders to select the most annoying among the seniors, I bet the debate wouldn't have ended to date. But time and tide wait for none.

An old sense of fear stalked us as we left for our summer vacation.

Chapter **4**	# Class VII # Part I – The Fear Factor

It was a vibrant day. A special Assembly was called. RamMohan was appointed as the house captain of Pallava House. The 7th graders were running scared. Kishore was sitting under the stairs. Or rather hiding. He had broken into a cold sweat.

"Kishore! Wake up will you!" It was his mother.

"Thank God, it was a dream!" thought Kishore, only to find that he peed in his pants during the nightmare he had.

"Summer vacations are over. Today is the last day. Get ready for breakfast now."

We had to report to school the next day. Few trains from different parts of the state brought the boys back to school. I boarded the Visakha Express at Miryalaguda. Kishore would join me at Guntur. The bad news was that RamMohan would also board at Guntur. Fear writ large on Kishore's face. I was lucky that I could sleep off before the train reached Guntur. And since I boarded from another station, I was in another compartment.

Confident that nobody would be able to find me, I slept comfortably. The funny part was that in the end we would all alight together at the same station and stay in the same house.

Well, I thought, *I will cross the bridge when I reach it. Let me sleep now.*

Kishore was waiting for the train. He was restless and jumped at every sound. He didn't even dare turn his head fearing he would sight RamMohan. He had argued and fought with his brother umpteen times, for informing Gagan and Harish about what RamMohan and his friends did to him. "*Our thoughts are like stray dogs which chase us as long as we are scared. The moment we stand still they simply fade away,*" his brother explained.

"*In your foolishness, you have put us into trouble for years now.*" Kishore sighed.

His brother had nothing to say now. He had tried consoling Kishore till yesterday.

"*Why do you think so much? I'll be leaving the school just a year ahead of them; till then I am there for you. Why do you worry?*"

"*You are not the one getting bullied here. Anyways, thanks for the favour, Bro.*"

Just then he saw RamMohan walking on the platform with his friends with a smile on his face. Kishore tried to hide behind his brother.

"*Look there, he is RamMohan. Look at him and his physique. His palm is like stone, I tell you.*"

"*You can only see RamMohan all around you. I see other seniors of grades 11 and 12 around. He won't dare harm you now. Relax!*" comforted his brother.

"*You bet!!*" retorted Kishore

The train arrived. All rushed towards the bogie. Kishore was boarding the train when he heard RamMohan behind him. "*Hey Kishore, I thought you will not be coming back to school this year. Feels good to see you back! We will have a good time in school. Have a good sleep tonight. Rambo must be coming as well, right?"*

"Yes, Master."

Kishore's brother felt sorry for him. *"Goodnight, Kishore."*

Kishore was on the berth, moving restlessly. *"You have screwed up all my nights,"* he mumbled looking back angrily.

We reached Vizianagaram station the next morning and boarded the school bus. Kishore and I were sitting together.

"So how was your vacation?" I enquired.

"It was great as long as RamMohan was out of my mind and a nightmare as and when I remembered him. It is torture- simply put. I couldn't breathe without thinking of RamMohan last night".

"I see, did he say, 'I'm going to bash you idiots, again' or what?" I joked.

"You ass! I have you to thank for my state. You escaped because of my idiot brother."

"I didn't ask your brother to interfere in this."

"Yeah Yeah, Kishore replied sarcastically *I'm the fool who saved your bloody butt, and, in turn, I am their main target now."*

"Two nights back I dreamt that RamMohan was appointed as our house captain."

I laughed aloud. *"Your dreams never come true so don't think too much about it now. Moreover, you are not alone in this. I am with you."*

As we reached the school entrance, 200 mts away from the school's administrative block and about 400 mts away from the playground our hearts raced.

Kishore took a deep breath. *"The countdown has begun."*

"So be it. Let it get over fast."

"Soon it will be payback time," whispered Kishore as we began walking towards our house. Our classmates joined us. We shared the fear of impending doom.

As we entered the house, we saw 6th graders with shining happy eyes. I nodded to Harsha; *"they look like -Alice in Wonderland. They come with loads of confidence and great pride for making it to the school. And then….!"*

Just then RamMohan walked past us with a cheery, *"Welcome to class 7 Rambo."*

"Now, do you feel the same?" enquired Harsha.

I replied, *"Why not? We have become seniors in a way. Though we have got to face our seniors now in the worst form of submission, it has become a part of our routine now. So, it doesn't bother me now."*

We were concerned about who would now move to senior house from class 9 of the Pallava House. We prayed that RamMohan and his friends would go to the senior house.

Just then, Bampu arrived. Bare-chested. Wearing just a lungi.

Everybody is a HERO in their individual capacity. *Only Bampu can help us now*, I thought.

"We have never really understood how significant our Bampu is," stated Suresh. Bampu has called the 9th graders to his office. *Who could be transferred to the senior house? More importantly, who would stay?*

Those thirty minutes that we spent outside Bampu's office seemed like ages. As time passed, we became edgy and then fearful.

Bampu ended the meeting. The 9th graders walked out and began hugging each other. We couldn't make out anything. We were desperate to know who is shifting to senior house. We paced towards the storeroom and stood there. Those shifting will soon move their trunks.

The ward boy of the house opened the storeroom. We saw RamMohan and his friends in front of the storeroom. Class 6 boys looked at us puzzled. They had no idea why we - the 7th graders, were so anxious. Rajesh spotted RamMohan walking out of the store-room lugging his trunk box. Just by Rajesh's expression, Kishore guessed that RamMohan was moving to the senior house.

Not only RamMohan, but his entire group shifted to the senior house. We couldn't believe our luck. We were in awe of Bampu. Out of gratitude, we decided not to reveal his nickname to juniors. We called him Bampu so often that we couldn't remember his real name. The name Bampu was in circulation for decades by then. We were aware that the juniors would eventually know. The problem was that except Bampu nobody knew his actual name and there was nobody who didn't know him as Bampu. His name was as popular as the Kohinoor diamond.

The next day a special assembly was convened. Naresh and Chandan were honored as the house captain and vice-captain of Pallava House. The day felt festive. The mood was jubilant. The class 7 students of the Pallava House were celebrating. Post-lunch, that day, our House Prefects called for a fall-in, addressed the house, and introduced the Token System formally. Now in class 7, both Harsha and I shared the same iron frame bunk-bed. The class 7 and 9 students occupied the extreme ends of their respective dormitories. Revanth and Bhuvan were relieved as they were no more part of the first file. Ramu and I didn't have to argue on who is taller anymore.

Every Monday during the PT hour, our canvas shoes were inspected by our senior Master Mr. Rao. Shiva a new 9th grader called me on Sunday evening.

"Hey Rambo, wash my shoes will ya?"

I couldn't take it. But I had no other choice. I had to. We, the 7th graders were always at the receiving end. I could tolerate no more. I just passed on the task to a 6th grader. We the 7th graders had a feeling that we were seniors to the new 9th graders by virtue of joining the school early. When Harsha saw this, he remarked *"this is why you are called Bloody Rambo. Only you can pull off such audacity."*

As a procedure, two 7th graders wake up everybody for PT in the morning. The next morning it was Kalyan's (Bison) and my turn, as duty boys, to wake up everybody for PT. The boys were in deep sleep and didn't hear the siren as they slept after a tiring day. It so happened that, we too were fast asleep and didn't wake up either for our duty or the siren. Fortunately, Naresh - the house captain woke up at 5:40 am just 20 minutes before the PT time and he shouted. *"Who are the duty boys?"*

Bison and I jumped out of our beds in shock and went running to Naresh.

"Yes, Master, we are the duty boys."

Annoyed he replied. *"I don't have enough time to bash you, idiots, now. Go and wake up everyone quickly and report to me after lunch."*

It was like an emergency drill. To add to our misery, we didn't have enough washrooms. There was a mad scramble for the eight available washrooms. If we were late, the school captain would ask our house captains to report to him. So, we sprinted to PT half-awake, messy but dressed and well almost on time.

Mr. Rao was present. We, the Pallavans were late by seven minutes. The school captain made us run 5 tracks (400 meters each) as punishment. Mr. Rao was vexed with our Prefects for our disregard for discipline.

That day during the class I kept the Token with me and spoke in Telugu wholeheartedly and informed everybody to speak in Telugu till lunch, as I had to report to Naresh anyway. If I kept the Token, we could avoid a scapegoat at least for a day. The day was pure joy for the boys. It was the first day they didn't worry about anyone giving them the Token. As lunch break approached, they felt sympathetic towards us.

Post-lunch we reported to Naresh.

He thundered, *"Had I not woken up, you idiots would have got me too punished. I feel you guys understand it only when you are put in such a situation. Do you?"*

"No Master."

"Kneel."

We immediately landed straight on our knees. Naresh slapped us black and blue. Chandan joined him. We had gone blank with pain.

"Can you see anything now?" asked Naresh.

"Yes, Master, we can see the stars," I replied.

"Right! Are these stars enough or do you like to see more?" asked Chandan.

"Enough Master," responded Bison.

"No, it's not enough. You guys deserve more. Do Murga[10] *during the pre-game study hour,"* Naresh dismissed us.

The Prefects had forgotten us. As we had to go for games, Naresh relieved us. We were not able to stand up. We sat on our desks to gain composure. In one hour of such squats, I could see the entire galaxy, and GS was searching if there was anything beyond it. It was 4.15 pm and we were frozen by sitting in Murga pose for an hour.

The next day during our craft class all of us were cutting wood into different shapes under the supervision of our craft master. When all were busy cutting, Nageswara Rao (alias Kaalia) a Kakatiyan was exploring his creativity in writing. Unfortunately, his creative writing skills were cut short by our craft master when he found Kaalia had written TOK on a piece of wood. The craft master, asked *"Kaalia, what are you writing on the wood?"*

"Token. Sir"

The class looked at him in awe. But the Craft Master wasn't impressed.

"Were you writing, TOKADA?"

We had to bite our tongue to control our laughter.

Kaalia looked surprised at the Craft Master and asked, *"Who is TOKADA Sir?"*

All of us immediately burst out into laughter. Our Craft Master couldn't take the humiliation and pounced on Kaalia like a hungry lion on a deer. He beat him left, right, and center to everybody's shock and terror.

[10.] Murga - ear squats (heads bent close to the knees, fingers on ears)

"How dare you ask me who is TOKADA, you idiot, rascal, scoundrel." He made Kalia kneel in the hot sun outside the class. Kaalia was in tears.

Immediately after class got over and Tokada left we rushed to Kaalia and consoled him. Kaalia responded in tears. *"What was my fault if he forgot what his actual name (Shobhan Babu) was, and identified himself so much with the name of TOKADA?"*

The entire class was in splits. Shobhan Babu, our Craft Master had lived up to his name - TOKADA.

The best thing that happened with us - the Pallavans of class 7 was that both our Prefects were more into academics. Our lives and sanity were spared.

Though there were several instances where we countered either RamMohan or his friends from Gupta House, we simply bowed our heads and ran to save ourselves. In time, we turned street-smart.

By then it had become a daily ritual for someone with the Token to report to either of the Prefects. One day it was Srinivas (a fat ass with chubby cheeks and round tummy) turn to report with the Token. He thought that reporting to Chandan who was interested in academics, would be sensible. He reported to Chandan. But unfortunately for him, Chandan was in a bad mood. He had faced the wrath of the school captain for his inefficiency in managing his responsibilities as prefect.

So, the moment Srinivas went to him with the Token, Srinivas was beaten black and blue and was shouted at. Finally, Chandan dismissed him by calling him a fat bastard. This didn't go down well with Srinivas. He was deeply hurt that Chandan called him 'Bastard'.

He was crying as he slumped over his bed. Suresh sympathized; *"Chandan shouldn't have used such a word."*

Srinivas cried out, *"Isn't HE a fat bastard?"*

We decided to keep him out of issues as he was vulnerable and simple.

As Srinivas was weeping, an old man came in asking for Srinivas. By the time we got to know who he was, he had reached Srinivas's bed.

He hugged Srinivas. *"What happened, my son?"*

Srinivas cried out, *"Grandpapa, Chandan called me a bastard."*

His grandfather was mad with anger. *"Who is he? Where is he?"*

"He is our House vice-captain who stays in the other dormitory," Srinivas replied.

"Doesn't matter, take me to him immediately," he yelled.

None of us could guess what would happen. Srinivas took him to Chandan, who was taking a nap. Srinivas's grandpa wasn't in any mood to let it go. He caught hold of his collar and pulled him up. Chandan was taken aback and asked with a tremor in his voice. *"Who are you? What are you doing here?"*

He saw Srinivas there by his side. Before he could understand the situation, he was slapped and shouted down by Srinivas's grandfather. He tried to speak but was slapped again. He just sat there in stunned silence.

Meanwhile, class 9th intervened and pacified Srinivas's grandfather and assured him that such incidents will not be repeated. Hearing the racket, Bampu entered the dormitory, in his usual bare-chested style. After he was appraised by Srinivas's grandfather, Bampu made Chandan apologize for his comments and saved grace. Once again Bampu became the show-stealer.

The issue was far from over. During games, we moved towards the ground. Our hearts were pounding. We had all been lucky, so far as RamMohan and his friends were concerned. We didn't expect captain Naresh or vice-captain Chandan to hurt us. But now that Chandan was humiliated, we might have to face severe consequences.

"I think we are into a problem now," commented Bhuvan.

I smiled, *"No Bhuvan, we are into a fresh problem now, as problems are not new to us."*

The next morning during PT it was apparent that they wouldn't spare us anymore. On Mondays, we had special Physical Training. On all other days, house Prefects took PT for their respective houses. They harassed us to the extreme. We were drained of energy with the physical exercise and fainted by the time PT got over. It was clear that we had black days ahead.

The winter vacations brought some respite.

Chapter **5**	**Class VII**
	Part II – Psychological Factors

Vacations are every child's favorite time. The cool and pleasant winters make ordinary days special and vacations splendid. Winters welcome Christmas and Sankranthi. Crops are harvested, beds feel cozy and the fireplace enticing. I belong to a farming family, from a small village of Kondrapole, in Nalgonda district in the erstwhile state of Andhra Pradesh.

The village rested on the Hyderabad-Guntur Highway. My home was next to a canal that flowed from the Nagarjuna Sagar dam that irrigates lakhs of acres of farmland. Villages that dotted its banks mostly grew paddy as there was enough water for paddy cultivation. Hordes of migrant workers worked in the fields during harvest.

Father cultivated about thirty acres of land. Part of it was leased. We employed two people to work in our fields. We had twenty cattle, including oxen to help in ploughing and buffaloes for mulching.

The entire village used to wake up to the song of the Bhagavad-Gita, coming from the Sri Rama temple. The temple was opposite to our house.

A highway ran between our house and the temple. Our home was warm and welcoming. Nobody left empty-handed or hungry.

We were five in all - three sisters and two brothers; I was the youngest. When the crop ripened and was ready to be harvested, we helped in gathering the crop along with the laborers which were then threshed by a tractor to separate paddy from straw. In the evening, we were paid ten rupees by father for our work. We loved the fields and playing in the soil.

In all, gathering paddy, threshing, and winnowing it for sale, took two weeks. In the end, we had a huge pile of dry straw for cattle feed that lasted till summer. Ours was a small, but beautiful house; the vast area was left for rearing cattle, piling straw, and a store-house for paddy. Mother loved plants, so she grew a variety of flowers, marigold, chamomile, lilies, jasmine, hibiscus, tomatoes, ladyfinger, chilly, bottle-gourd, bitter-gourd, beans, and cucumber all grew in plenty. We had fruit trees and decorative plants too. Mother raised some poultry too.

We played cricket in an open area – between our house and the cattle shed. By evening children from neighbouring homes gathered here to play. The place reverberated with joy and laughter. The place spoke of abundance – birds chirping, lazing cattle, playful children, and the laughter from grownups.

After harvest, we and our friends would catch a movie at Miryalaguda. With paltry pocket money we traveled, snacked, and watched a movie. Prema Paavuraalu (Maine Pyaar Kiya) was my first memorable movie in the theatre and since then I became a diehard fan of Salman Khan.

We played cricket with rubber balls. Since we didn't have enough to buy a cricket ball, we collected plastic covers - especially those empty licensed liquor packets - and melted them in a fused bulb, and let it cool for a day. When we broke the bulb later, we had our ball ready. We were crazy and innovative.

There were hardly one or two televisions in a village. Regional movies were aired once a week. The entire village, especially kids, gathered in homes that had television, especially on Sunday evenings. We lived our childhood when the Ramayana, Mahabharata, and Sri Krishna were aired on Doordarshan. We were a spiritual lot and were crazy about archery.

I looked forward to vacations because I loved to play around the village - chasing birds, swimming in the canal. I relished raw buffalo milk, homemade cheese, butter, and ghee. My friends and I played in the fields, frequented the temple and waited to light lamps in the evenings. I helped my mother feed cattle and in chasing her hens to their coops. My home was full of activity, energy, and radiance.

For me, leaving home was always difficult, particularly when life at school got tougher. The mere thought of school made me uncomfortable; but as it goes, time and tide wait for none; vacations were over, and it was time to board our trains to school.

Our faces bore the same expression. We felt like it was the beginning of our end. We couldn't understand what to do and how to escape from PT. Some began getting admitted to the Sick Bay to avoid PT, but that was a temporary relief, maybe for a day or a two. Those who got the Token were ruthlessly bashed. It created a situation of panic; there seemed no way out. We felt like we were living in hell.

One day Revanth (our Notice Board insect) came running. He looked happy.

"Hey guys, I have got great news for all of you."

Nobody was interested. Our house might have come first in academics or some other activity.

"How does it help us? Big deal!"

Revanth smiled. *"It's not a big deal; it's a very big deal."*

"What's that dude?"

"The school administration is about to introduce Karate, that too during PT hours," stated Revanth.

"That's the best news we ever had since the beginning of this academic year," replied Bhuvan.

"Indeed!" agreed Harsha.

We were jubilant.

"When is it going to start?" asked an excited Kalyan.

"Coming Monday. Just three more days to go. The enrollment starts tomorrow."

"Yippee!!!" cheered Revanth.

By next Monday, everybody from class 7 had enrolled for karate. The PT class which was like hell just until a day ago for us had turned into heaven now. Still, we were always alert, to avoid being caught by seniors for breaking some rule.

We were like mice, under constant threat of being caught by the cat. Since we couldn't find freedom in the house, we started enjoying the present - in any opportunity, time, or place. Bampu was the Science teacher for the A section and he was quite liberal in giving marks. He was so generous that few boys even scored 101 and 102 out of 100 while totaling. Some students used to add ½ mark or 1 mark with red pens and then tell Bampu that there is a totaling mistake and score higher.

Mr. Ramesh was the science teacher for section B. When someone used to ask for marks saying that half of the answer was right. He used to say, *"If there is a question asking, 'how many legs does a cow have', for 4 marks, and if you write 'two' as the answer, should I give you 2 marks?"*

Our Social teacher Mr. Sarvesh who taught us Geography was a short and sweet man. His head was bald and was called Globe. Globe had a photographic memory; he corrected students while they read the textbook, without even looking at the book once.

The mango season had begun. There were over 200 mango trees in our school which were leased every year. Every Saikorian had eyed the mango orchard when we visited the school campus for our interviews. Since then, we wait for the mango season. But the one major hurdle was the sentries, posted by the new contractors every year.

Sentries guarded the orchard with long sticks. Very rarely did they catch a mango thief. We were good at fleeing, most of the time. Our greatest worry was the sticks they held. They threw them at us like javelin sticks. So, it was risky as the sticks could hurt and cause us irreparable damage.

We were cautious while stealing mangoes. Banganpalli mangoes were everybody's favorite. Once as Kalyan and I went to the post office, we saw no sentry around. There were plenty of Banganpalli mangoes hanging from low branches. I was lightweight. I quickly climbed the tree and started throwing mangoes down. Kalyan was picking them. Suddenly, a stick came flying from nowhere and landed beside Kalyan.

Sensing danger, he escaped. The sentry came running to pick his stick. But all that running had tired him, and he sat under the tree. I was still quietly sitting on the tree. In the silence, I could even hear my heartbeat and was worried if the sentry could hear it too. I prayed for someone to come to steal mangoes nearby so that the sentry would be distracted. Kalyan returned with Suri and pretended to pluck mangoes and started running away from the sentry.

The moment the sentry ran a few paces I crash-landed behind him. By the time the sentry realized what happened; we vanished and reached the house in no time. The sentry followed us, but he wasn't allowed to enter the house. Thankfully we were saved for the day. Not only that, I had managed to fill in my tucked shirt with as many mangoes as I could before jumping off the tree.

The major spaces of threat, to us were the tuck shop, open-air theatre, special assemblies, and all such places where we came in proximity with

RamMohan or his friends. On a Saturday evening, Harsha and I walked towards the tuck shop to pick up a chakodi packet -a crazy snack stuff for Rs. 2/-. We saw RamMohan standing at the shop. I insisted that we leave.

As we tried to avoid him, RamMohan called my name. I didn't want to face him and kept walking. RamMohan called again. This time Harsha stopped and pulled my hand. As we turned around, Harsha pointed towards RamMohan that he was calling me. I then didn't have a choice, but to go. By then, RamMohan was annoyed as he knew that we were running away, knowing that he was calling us.

I went rushing to RamMohan. "*Master, did you call me?*"

That annoyed RamMohan further. "*You bastard, didn't you hear me calling you?*"

I held my nerve. "*No Master. Had I heard you, I would have come.*"

"*I know it fucker. Don't bluff. Now that you are going to class 8, it looks you have started acting smart,*" barked RamMohan.

"*Now go and report to Naresh that you didn't respond to me when I called you and that I asked you to report to him.*"

I got really worried now. "*Master, I didn't hear you. Please forgive me.*"

"*Let that be decided by Naresh,*" snorted RamMohan, and left.

I walked up to Naresh and reported.

Naresh gave me a lightning slap. "*I'm fed up with you fuckers. Probably this is the last slap of mine to you at the end of this academic session, now just fuck off.*"

Keeping my head low, I rushed back to my dormitory. Harsha called me. I didn't look back.

It didn't matter to me that the academic year ended with a slap. What mattered was that it ended. With every ending, there is a new beginning.

In the junior house, class 8 was nothing short of heaven. We left for our summer vacations on a high note.

Chapter 6

Class VIII

Part I – Freedom from Within

Paddy is harvested both in summers and in winters. But any parallel between the two seasons ends there. These seasons – as far as vacations are concerned, were entirely different. After harvest, fields were kept fallow till monsoons. During the two months of summer, we lived cricket in open fields. Winter vacations welcomed gully cricket. All-day we played bet matches with the neighbouring gully mates.

I owned a cricket bat. Every morning by six, my friends whistled for me and my granny would grumble, *"You idiots, won't you even let him have his breakfast?"* I quietly passed the bat to them over the wall and then sneaked to the fields. We had no regard for time, hunger, or even the scorching tropical Sun. We returned to our homes only when one of our grandmothers came looking for us with a stick. Game over; we dispersed at the sound of the loud rumble from a mother or grandma.

We roamed nearby forests with our phony bow and arrows and practiced archery by aiming at birds. We would rarely hit a bird. We imagined we were Lord Sri Rama. We loved the thick groves of trees. The overgrowth drew a canopy over the sky and sheltered us from the blistering summer heat.

We frequented small hillocks surrounding our village and collected wild fruits and insects, fished in ponds and canals as they began drying up in summers. We allowed our cattle to graze in the open. We hung from carts driven by bullocks and also traveled in them. The carts ferried cow dung manure to the fields to prepare the soil for sowing.

We paced over two kilometers every day to the lone house that had a television set in the village until father finally decided to purchase a television. What a day it was! It was the first T.V. on our street. Father had brought a small portable black and white Onida T.V.

Now that was quite a thing- to own a TV.

I began watching Hindi movies aired over DD National on Friday nights. Amitabh Bachchan was the man we looked out for.

One day a snake tried to make its way out from our boundary wall, towards the canal. I tried to scare the snake by yelling at it. Sensing the commotion, the snake quickly slid back into the stone wall. My friends scared me by saying that it was a cobra and it would take vengeance.

Scared, I went and complained to mother. She smiled when she heard my concern. "*Let's fix it,*" she offered. She got a stick and a jute string. I was puzzled.

"*Look for a frog. Let's catch one fast.*"

"*Frog!!! But why?*"

"*Just do what I say,*" ordered mother.

We found a frog, caught it, and tied it to the string.

"*Where did you see the snake?*"

We were curious to know what she was up to. I pointed out the hole, "*There it is ma.*"

She poked the stick with the frog in front of the snake hole.

The frog began jumping, to free itself. It was the best bait for a snake. Mother stood patiently with a stick and asked everyone to stay quiet. Three minutes had passed. The snake was finally tempted. It slithered out and opening its mouth wide, at one go, swallowed the frog.

The snake's mouth was full. Its body was focused on hunting and eating. With a single mighty blow, to its hood, the snake fell flat on the ground. Children standing there applauded. Mother was relieved. I hugged her.

"Never panic. Ever. Think patiently. There is no problem without a solution."

Her advice went straight home. I knew. There would be a solution. Surely.

Life becomes miserable to those who look at it as an obstacle and a miracle to those who look at it as an opportunity. The choice is ours.

Summer vacations were over. It was time to return to school.

Unlike 7th grade, we were relaxed. We were seniors. The hunted were becoming hunters. We began the year from a place of strength and not threat. The moment the source of fear is gone, new confidence creeps in and that was apparent in the faces of all the class 8 guys.

After schooling here for two years, it was for the first time, that, we could shout out and say whatever we could without fear of scrutiny. We felt alive. We knew that we could breathe inside the house. Our perspective had changed completely. Whenever we called out for somebody from class 6, the fear in their eyes made us realize - *You can't be what you haven't experienced.*

We had journeyed from grade 6 to 8. Unknown to us, our perspective had completely changed. To our credit, the responsibility of making a house Cock House fell on the class 8 students in the junior house. It was a year of showcasing our competitive edge, brilliance, and spirit. Our batch from the Pallava house had amazing sportsmen and academicians.

The major contenders for the Cock House at the junior level were the Pallavans and the Kakatiyans. The Pandyans and the Mauryans had the fighting spirit but were no match. They tried to mitigate losses by scoring high in extracurricular activities. Kakatiyans had Arabind who looked like Gulliver among the Lilliputs when we joined our grade 6 and Vikal Sharma who had a great physique with amazing athleticism.

Our Pallava house had ace players like B. Kiran. B.K. was short and lean. He was the best in all games he chose to play. He was amazing in track events; it seemed he just flew with the wind. Kishore, my buddy was B.K's partner in football. Sumadhur was amazing at indoor games and football. Karthik was great at chess and cricket. Virat, Mahidhar, Suri were all good athletes and sportsmen. I was good at swimming and cricket.

All the houses were equally good at academics. The Pandyans and the Mauryans always tried to put in their best in all debates, extempore speeches, quizzes, dramatics, and so on to compensate for their dismal performance in sports when compared to their competitors. But we Pallavans were achievers in these too. We also had amazing academicians like Karthik, Ramu, Pradeep, Sumadhur, and others.

We had developed intense loyalty towards our houses on account of playing sports. The team spirit was on an all-time high. The classroom seemed to split into four teams even during academics. We outperformed in one sport after another, in both indoor and outdoor. We had gained a winning streak.

It was the day of the Volleyball finals. The Pallavans vs the Kakatiyans. The Pallavans were up by one set and it looked as if they would wrap up the match in the second set itself. What happened later was unexpected. Arabind volleyed the ball to Rajesh. Rajesh who hadn't had the ball volleyed to him until then hit the ball out of the court in a parabola.

When the Kakatiyans saw his skill, they targeted him repeatedly and stayed back in the game by winning the second set. We understood that we were being attacked on our weak link, Rajesh. So, we replaced him with Vamsi (Porcupine). But it was too insignificant and too late a change. The replacement was no better. Our team had to go defensive and in the process of covering for him, we lost the match. We also lost to the Pandyans who were the underdogs in the Hockey finals.

Except for hockey and volleyball, we, Pallavans swept the remaining outdoor trophies. We outperformed other teams in most of the swimming races. The major contenders in swimming were Kamal and Sudhakar (my cousin) from Pandya house who scored medals in Butterfly and Backstroke. Even in indoor games, the Pallavans routed all other houses in chess and table tennis. Mauryans managed to win at carrom.

As the days passed, the entire school slowly started contracting sore eyes. One after the other the boys began getting admitted to the Sick Bay. The Sick Bay was full and few recreation rooms were turned into quarantine centers for those affected. Two of the 8th graders from the Pallava house too were infected. Kalyan and Virat or the American and the Indian Bison as we called them.

The Sick Bay felt like a recreation center for us. Most of the time the Sick Bay was filled with class 9 and 10 students from the senior houses and class 7 from the junior houses. It was as if ailments knew whom to impact! But this time, it impacted many students across all classes. But only the students from classes 7, 8, 9, and 10 got admitted to Sick Bay. It was a heaven for those who got admitted there as they were not under anyone's scanner.

One of the most popular and youth-centric love stories of the time was released that week. The movie Prema Desam was in Telugu. The movie was a dubbed version of the Tamil original Kadhal Desam. It was later dubbed into Hindi too- Duniya Dilwalon Ki. The music was composed by A.R. Rehman, and it took the youth by storm. Mustaffa-Mustaffa, a song that was based on friendship was a smash hit and it was often played in the school mess.

The movie had catchy songs and starred newcomers Abbas and Vineet with Tabu. The film was the center of gossip at school and was widely watched. For those who wanted to watch the movie, infection and logging into Sick Bay was a God-sent opportunity as no Duty Master ever cross-checked those in Sick Bay during roll-call. Taking advantage, most of the 9 and 10 graders watched the movie, returning to give rave reviews.

The two Pallavan Bisons were admitted to Sick Bay, and couldn't resist the movie. They quietly sneaked out and watched the movie. It was the greatest feat so far in the history of the school. Until then, no one below class 9 had ever bunked to watch a movie. By the time they returned, they had become a sensation. The news of them bunking spread like wildfire. Most of us were in awe of them as if they were war heroes.

They wanted to share gossip about the movie, but before they could break the story, they were informed that they had to report to the Gupta house class 12 boys. They were shocked as to how the news could spread so far and so fast. No wonder they were called Bisons. Thickheads! How could they forget whom they were with, in the Sick Bay?

They had to pay the price for their naivety. Grade 8 boys bunking school was a new record and now class 12 boys had asked them to report. It was walking straight into the lion's mouth.

Chapter **7**	**Class VIII** **Part II – Sensing Trouble** **Around the Corner**

Until that day the juniors had never dared venture into or even look at the senior houses. The senior and junior houses were about 100 meters apart. The place in between nested a beautifully landscaped garden. The Bisons were ordered to report at the Gupta house.

Hell is not another place.

Here. Or there.

It is inside us.

If we choose to live anything other than peace. Or love.

We live our hell depending on the intensity of fear that we see or imagine.

They approached the house with trepidation.

"Virat, I want to turn back."

"Turn back where Kalyan? It is better we get it over with."

"They kept the 9th & 10th graders busy too," observed Kalyan as they watched boys walk briskly running errands for their seniors.

"Do you even see anybody with a smile? They look like they are living in hell."

Faces - expressionless. Conduct - cold and distant. Kalyan trembled as dread overtook the superficial feeling of bravado with which he had decided to report.

They reached the entrance of the house. They heard the resounding sound of slaps. The place had gone quiet.

RamMohan was standing with his head bowed. A 12th grader raised his hand to slap him. Again and again and again.

He looked at the Bisons with disdain.

"Where the hell are we?" whispered Virat (Indian Bison) to Kalyan (American Bison).

"Exactly! There you are. Hell. We are in hell. Just there."

Just then, Mahi of class 10, saw them standing and looking everywhere.

"What brings you here?"

"Master, Naidu from class 12 asked us to report."

"But why?"

"Because we bunked to watch PremaDesam," replied Virat.

"Oh! You two are the new trendsetters! You have become the talk of the school."

Kalyan nodded; head bowed.

"Well then, do you know Master Naidu?"

"No Master" replied both.

"Go to the senior dormitory. Naidu's bed is the last to your left. Good luck."
Mahi turned around and left.

Their pulse raced as they stepped into the senior dormitory. As they walked towards Master Naidu's bed, they saw class 9 and 10 students beaten and kicked by their seniors. They were a few paces away from Master Naidu's bed when Master Rupesh (vice-captain of the Gupta House from class 11) stopped them.

"Who are you and who called you?"

Their voice trembled as they explained.

Rupesh laughed out loud and looked at Naidu. *"Boss, the Love Bugs are here."*

"Yeah, yeah, let them come," replied Naidu.

Even before they said anything, a lightning slap hit their cheeks.

"How dare you, bastards?"

The Bisons bowed their heads.

"With whose permission did you bunk?" asked Naidu.

They had no answer.

"Do you realize that you are still in class 8th?" asked Naidu.

"Yes Master."

"I somehow feel that you don't."

Well then get on to my cupboard,

In no time Virat was on it.

"Kneel down."

Virat had no time to think. He jumped from the cupboard and landed on his knees.

He could have broken his knees. He yelped in pain as he landed.

Naidu looked at Kalyan, *"Slap Virat."*

Kalyan was shocked.

Tears rolled down his cheeks as he watched Virat's plight. He couldn't immediately respond to Naidu.

A series of slaps on both his cheeks rendered him stunned and senseless. His face had swollen and his lips bruised. Blood oozed from the corner of his mouth. Virat looked shocked.

"Slap him," ordered Naidu again.

Kalyan slapped Virat hard. On the face. Both cheeks.

Then it was Virat's turn to slap Kalyan.

Both wept simultaneously. They had to slap each other continuously.

Even the onlookers rendered speechless. In that room that day, life was robbed of dignity. Boys from good families. Students compete to join the school. For this? Nobody interfered. The experience was sickening both to the viewers and the victims.

Virat could not stand.

"What did you think of yourself? You fuckers!" shouted Naidu.

The juniors could not speak.

"Do you think you are loverboys? Did you want to watch a love story in grade 8 to shag?"

"No Master."

"Just remember that you are in class 8."

"Sorry Master, please forgive us."

"This is just a demo. Let this message spread to everyone as a warning. If we receive any complaints in the future, consider yourself dead. Understood?" he shouted.

"Yes Master."

"Now get the hell out of here!"

They wanted to vanish from there but were helpless. Particularly Virat. He couldn't stand.

Naidu was alarmed. *"Rest on any of the 9th grader's beds for a while and then go."*

"Okay, Master," they replied as they limped out of the room.

The 9th and 10th graders around felt sorry, but they maintained that Virat and Kalyan have committed a grave error. Nobody dared to call out the bullying of the seniors.

They flopped flat on their beds without speaking a word. Their bruises and Virat's limp spoke volumes of what they had gone through.

"Thank God, I didn't go with them," gasped Suri. *"They asked me, but luckily since I wasn't in the Sick Bay, I told them that I can't risk bunking."*

It was a Black day. The boys were beaten to a pulp. Nevertheless, who gave these bullies any authority? And worse still, they couldn't complain. What if the school took action against Virat and Kalyan for bunking in the first place?

That incident set a precedent for a fear psychosis among us. A shadow had fallen. Like dark sullen sticky grey smoke. Of drooping shoulders. Blank faces. Expressionless eyes and fear. Fear - that Virat and Kalyan saw on many faces in the senior house that day.

"What would we do when we shift into the senior house next year?"

That is when we realized, the power of Bampu. This was the first time that we didn't laugh while speaking about him. Many of us were sleepless that night. Those who slept had vicious nightmares of being sent to the Gupta House in their class 9.

Life moved in events and dragged in the boring days in between.

Martina Hingis of Switzerland had won the Women's Singles Australian Open Test Championship. At 16 she was the youngest to do so since 1887. Her picture holding the trophy was published on the front page of The Hindu.

It was the first time I saw her. Gorgeous. Pretty. Beautiful hair. Perhaps this is love. The warmth feel that hit my stomach when I saw her. And that, every time I saw her picture, I would smile and smile and blush. I was crazy about her.

I couldn't forget her even during class that day. Post-lunch the first thing I did was to cut out her picture and keep it in my cupboard. I was just three years younger than she probably was. We could get married one day. A staunch critic of Sachin Tendulkar, I had begun to look up to him now that he had married Anjali, elder to him by five years. I could definitely marry Martina!

I was a crazy fan of Azharuddin and Salman. I would tussle with fans of Sachin and Shahrukh who were equally popular or more. I didn't care.

Now Martina had become my priority. I was an ardent tennis fan; though I never played. I collected her pictures from wherever I could.

One day as our class attended the library, I found an amazing poster of Hingis, in the Sportstar magazine.

"Oh, God! She's so pretty!"

I couldn't resist.

I wanted that poster at any cost. I looked around. The librarian wasn't around. Very carefully and softly I tore out the page, folded it, and put it in my pocket. I thought I would pass unnoticed. But my hands trembled. I knew what I had just done wasn't right. But I couldn't help it. I needed to have the picture.

The library period was over and we began putting back our books and moving towards the door. Our face is the mirror of our thoughts. The librarian had one look at me and was sure that I was up to something.

"Hey there!"

I looked at him terrified.

"What magazine did you read?"

I couldn't lie. *"Sportstar, Sir."*

"Can you please bring me the magazine?" he suggested.

I was slowly breaking into perspiration. I had no choice but to do as directed.

The librarian quickly turned its pages.

My discomfort was evident. I was restless. He saw the place where I had torn the page and asked me regarding the missing page.

I stood as if at gunpoint and realized that there was no point in trying to bluff.

I took the page out of my pocket. *"Here it is, Sir."*

"Why did you do that?"

"For the love of Hingis, Sir."

The librarian leaned back on his chair and straightened his glasses.

He looked at me sagely, "*There is nothing wrong in being a fan of someone or being in love with someone, but then, for you to be the one for whom you love, you should be ONE among a Crore and not someone among a Crore.*"

My eyes smarted as reality sunk in. "*I'm sorry, Sir. Please take it back.*"

The librarian patted me nonchalantly and concluded, "*Now that you already torn it, keep it, but don't ever repeat it.*" I was relieved to hear that and responded, "*I'll never Sir,*" and vanished in a second. That was the last poster of Hingis I added to my collection. I realized my foolishness and smiled at myself.

The Drama competition was nearing. All the houses had amazing actors and entertainers. There was plenty of talent. The major genres, of dramatics, were comedy, emotion, drama, suspense, and horror. We Pallavans, choose comedy-drama, with Suri and me at loggerheads. The skit went on to become a runaway success, and Suri was adjudged as the best actor. This was an area, which other houses eyed, but we didn't let it slip away from our hands.

In athletics, Pallavans and Kakatiyans were neck-to-neck in competition. The Pandyans and the Mauryans also struggled to save their faces. What mattered was not about who won or who lost, it was all about how much of our inner ability we could explore. In that aspect, both the Mauryans and the Pandyans put in their heart and soul to go beyond their limitations and performed their best.

Arabind-The Gulliver and Vikal Sharma-The Handsome hunk from the Kakatiya house and B.K.-The Ace and Virat-The Indian Bison from the Pallava House were the major contenders for the championship. Arabind took maximum advantage of his height to win most of the track and field events. In the rest, B.K. took the lead closely followed by Vikal and Virat.

The tally was often close. No house had a comfortable lead. If Pallava was leading at the end of one event, the Kakatiyans would catch up by the end of the next event. Everybody performed their best for the glory of their houses. At the end of the day, Arabind managed to become the champion with great difficulty with stiff competition from his housemate Vikal and the Ace Athlete B.K from the Pallava house.

With every success, our spirit and confidence increased. Our house was always filled with positive vibes and energy. It was a time of our journey, where we were living our lives to the fullest and the joy was radiating from us. Everyone was doing great. Be it in academics, sports, extracurricular activities, spending time with their buddies, etc. we were extracting as much as we wanted to from life. Nobody ever wished to go to class 9.

Though we cannot stop time, we can certainly make every moment count, by making them memorable. Our days in class 8 were passing fast. We were happy for all that we had accomplished during the year, but at the same time, we were unsure what the next year would bring.

We were leaving for our summer vacation. We wished each other luck and prayed that we would be retained in the junior house itself. Though it felt unrealistic, there was no harm in hoping, or wishing, or praying. We left the rest to Bampu.

By God, only Bampu knew who was going to be retained in the junior house.

Chapter **8**	**Class IX**
	Part I – A New Beginning

We had progressed to the 9th grade. We lived three years at school here; understanding undercurrents, fighting, and adapting for survival. Yet nobody had spine enough to stand up to the 11th and 12th graders of the senior house. We knew them well by now. We progressed together. They only grew more vile, wicked, and smarter. We learned to support each other and adapt.

We boarded our trains. We stood unfortunate. We were the best here. We competed for our place for a better life and today we dreaded to walk to school. It was a restless journey for us. Our faces reflected the despair we were in. The boys who graduated from 10th were traveling with us. They seemed to be on cloud nine. It seemed like they had the world under their feet. Two contrasting lives at the same place.

Life's learnings from the same event were diverse for different people. The train chugged in. We were in a state of panic and clung close for courage.

"Did you see RamMohan?" enquired Kishore.

"Hahaha… you think of only him."

"It's all because of you. You Arsehole."

"Don't worry about him. I am sure you will stay in the junior house."

"We watched the school bus turn in towards the station."

The 11th graders seemed like huge giants to us. Big and menacing. They looked happy. My classmates looked restless and anxious. The 10th graders – now deemed as seniors, had juniors to fall back upon. As the bus rolled into the schools' main entrance, we the 9th graders were in trepidation.

RamMohan called my name as we alighted the bus.

"Who among you is joining Gupta house?"

"I am sure about myself, Master, but not about others."

"You seem to be all charged to join senior house."

"I feel Bampu is clear in that aspect, Master."

"That's good. We will be waiting for you guys," smiled RamMohan as he turned and walked away

"Sure, Master." I replied.

I was walking to the Pallava house when my classmates surrounded me.

"What did RamMohan say?"

"RamMohan remarked that they are waiting for our arrival."

"Oh!"

My friends grew anxious again.

"These guys are gonna screw us up. Why the hell did I join this school?" murmured Bhuvan.

Rajesh laughed, *"To get yourself fucked."*

We laughed together.

"It's good we laugh off this day. Who knows where we will be in a short while?" piped Suresh

Virat joined in, *"That's true."*

Revanth wanly added, *"I don't know."*

"We know that," said Manohar.

"RamMohan is my boss," pushed Vamshi.

"You bastard," everyone shouted at him.

"You are the one who got everyone fucked," berated Kishore.

We walked in silence for breakfast.

"This might be our last meal together this year," mused Pradeep.

"Yes," agreed everybody.

As we ate breakfast, Bampu entered the mess.

"Here comes our fate," I declared looking at Bampu.

"You couldn't be more correct," observed Suresh.

"Let's eat to our heartful."

"Only heartful is possible with these two dosas, not stomach full."

"Yes," agreed Virat.

"Only our Bampu can have his stomach full as he can have extra dosas unlike us," I added dryly. Everyone burst laughing.

"How can they serve 9ᵗʰ graders two dosas like they serve the 6ᵗʰ grade?"

"That's true," added Ramu.

Back in our dormitories, nobody unpacked.

We waited for Bampu, the Yamraj[11] himself. Meanwhile, Apparao (the house ward-boy) opened the storeroom door to hand over trunks of the boys shifting to senior house.

Sri Rama of grade 8 was a close friend of mine.

"Boss, what do you think?" he asked.

"I am prepared," I replied.

"But why, Boss?"

"Do you think I stand a chance?"

"I don't know."

"But I do know," I replied flippantly.

[11.] Yamraj- Hindu God of death

A runner from Bampu's office came with a message for us. He had summoned us. Our last ill-fated encounter with him still haunted us. Flashes of '*Who is Bampu?*' kept playing on our minds.

We entered his office and stood there.

Quietly.

Huddled together for comfort.

For a change, Bampu was fully dressed.

"Good to see a change before we leave," I muttered under my breath.

"Thank you all," Bampu began; *"It was only because of your team spirit that our House is going to be declared as the Cock House."* We jumped with joy.

Bampu continued, *"But as a tradition, we need to send eight of you to Gupta House for this academic year."* The room became gloomy again. *"I know nobody wants to go to senior house. But there is no choice."* Bampu sighed.

The silence was broken when Bampu announced Ramu and Pradeep as the House Prefects. We cheered and congratulated them.

He continued, what about you, *"Ring leader Ramakrishna, are you ready to expand your ring?"*

"Why not, Sir!" I responded.

He called out names. *"Suresh, Virat, Rajesh, Manohar, Vamshi, Revanth, and Bhuvan."*

The room was silent. Nobody knew how to react. We held each other's hands in solidarity.

His motive behind this selection was very apparent. Bampu wanted to get rid of those who bothered him and those boys who weren't academically bright. The only contribution junior house grade 9th could make towards improving Cock House scores was academic performance. Though he wanted to get rid of a few more, the count was limited to a max of eight so he did the best he could.

As we went back to our dormitory, I patted Kishore, *"Didn't I tell you that you will be left behind."*

Kishore was emotional. *"I am sorry for you, bro."*

"Don't worry about me. I am an arsehole. I can fit anywhere."

Kishore laughed wholeheartedly at the joke. *"I know you are not just an arshole but an ISO Certified arshole."*

We hugged with the assurance that we would meet each other next year in the 10th grade as Guptans. Our trunks were waiting for us.

As we strode to the Gupta house, we reminisced about how anxious we were while traveling to school the day before. We accepted that we indeed belong to the Gupta house and will now live with our seniors. The universe had tested us and taught us to overcome fear and grow in confidence to deal with tough situations.

We crossed the pillars of the house and reached a signboard *'Welcome to Gupta House'*.

"Even Hell has a Welcome Board!" we muttered. We saw a couple of class 11 and 12 students moving around in their vests showing their toned physique. Every time we saw these boys and their muscles, we could only imagine the hefty blows they would rain on us. Our future seemed like a dark shadow. One of the seniors passing by asked, *"So are you the chosen ones?"*

"Yes, Master," we responded.

We wondered. *Chosen for what?*

Just then Paparayudu appeared. *"Hey! Good to see you guys here."*

"Thank you, Boss," we responded.

He is Narayana, our house warden, pointing at the gentleman standing a little away. *"You can put your trunk boxes in and occupy your double bunk beds at the end of the dormitory."*

Unlike in the junior houses where the dormitories were earmarked for juniors and seniors, here few 11th graders shared junior dormitories because numbers grew after the admission of new 9th students. Moreover, only a quarter of the 9th graders join senior houses.

The 10th graders gave us a grand welcome. And then there was a call.

"*9th class.*"

Bhuvan took off like a bullet to attend to the caller.

It's only been thirty minutes since we arrived, and the first call had already come. In Gajapati house the first call took only thirty seconds. We were expected to attend to calls 24/7 with utmost importance for the next two years.

Bhuvan returned. "*Guys, RamMohan has asked us to fall in immediately.*"

We rushed to the kabaddi court. As we fell in line, the seniors passing by welcomed and wished us. RamMohan arrived at the Kabaddi court wearing a pair of trousers and a vest. He leaned forward on a hanging wire; his biceps shot up. There was no doubt that he was muscular and fit and now a bit taller than the last time we saw him.

"*So finally, your day has come! How is Bampu doing?*" enquired RamMohan.

"*He has grown broader, Master,*" responded Rajesh.

"*So have you,*" RamMohan smiled.

We smiled in relief.

Rupesh, the house captain of the Gupta House from class 12 joined RamMohan. We greeted him.

"*Do you guys know me?*" asked Rupesh.

"*Yes, Master.*"

"*Ok, That's good. But how?*"

"*You are our house captain, Master,*" replied Revanth our in-house BBC.

"*That's good. So, who is the vice-captain?*" asked RamMohan.

"*It has not been officially declared, Master.*"

"*It's me, you fucking bastards,*" chided RamMohan. We were stunned.

"*Yes, RamMohan is going to be our vice captain,*" confirmed Rupesh.

"*Ok, Master,*" we replied.

"*Now you are ninth graders. No need of calling us `Master`, you may call us `Boss`.*"

"*Yes, Boss,*" we followed in unison.

"*These guys are too fast, RamMohan.*"

"*Yes, Boss, we know them better,*" replied RamMohan.

No one from class 9 spoke. "*As I wasn't there in the junior house in class 9, please introduce yourself.*"

I began, "*Boss, I am Rambo.*"

'*Rambo? Is that your name?*" asked Rupesh.

"*Sorry Boss, I am Rama and I am called Rambo.*"

"*I see! Rambo. Only with time, we will get to know the real Rambo in you.*"

"*Boss, I am Revanth and called BBC and Kutchu.*"

"*Boss, I am Bhuvan, called Bomber.*"

"*Boss, I am Vamshi, called Porcupine.*"

Rupesh interrupted, "*I can see from your hair that you are the best porcupine.*"

Virat exclaimed, "*Boss I am Virat, called Indian Bison.*"

"*Why specific breed again?*" asked RamMohan.

"*American Bison is there in Pallava House Boss,*" replied Virat.

"*Boss, I am Suresh, called as Suri.*"

"*Boss, I am Rajesh. They call me Razia.*"

"*The name suits you,*" smiled Rupesh.

"*Boss, I am Manohar and people call me Crazy Man'.*

"*Very apt.*"

RamMohan's voice was now low and serious. "*Now that you are used to the rules of the game, just play on and don't ever be caught for wrong reasons, like indiscipline or disobeying the orders of your seniors.*"

He quickly added, "*If we come across any such complaint, I am going to bash you, idiots. Unlike the junior house, where only the Prefects are privileged to punish the juniors here the seniority is flattened. Shoulder flaps don't mean much here. So be careful,"* warned Rupesh.

"Now disperse."

During lunch, Bhuvan, Revanth, and I occupied the first file like we used to. But unlike the junior houses, we didn't fear the '*Stop There*'. The 9th and 10th graders moved in files for reporting on all activities. The 11th and 12th graders would join as they pleased - always late. There was constant fear of being punished, on flimsy grounds, or not obeying egoistic demands.

Can anybody be so foolish enough not to obey the orders? It wasn't just impossible but unimaginable. Even the Token system was not there in senior houses. What set apart 11th & 12th graders was their school uniform. They wore full-length trousers. Others including 10th graders wore shorts.

Post-lunch, the new Guptans, caught up with their Pallavan 9th grade mates.

"Kishore?"

"Yes, Rambo."

"I am sorry."

"Why?"

"I criticized your dream in class 7th. It has come true now."

"Is it! Oh! Which dream?" enquired Kishore.

"Your dream of RamMohan being selected as Prefect. I think you predicted the future dude. In a way, it's good that he didn't become a Prefect then. Now Prefect or not doesn't make much of a difference in any way. But the best thing I still find in RamMohan is, he still says, I am going to bash you idiots and I hope he continues to say so without actually kicking our butt." I quipped.

"I know how it feels when you actually get kicked on, You arsehole!" We laughed together and left for our houses.

We soon got used to the quirks and difficulties of the life we now lived.

Bhuvan took to the forefront in attending to calls from seniors.

The reason was when nobody responded Bhuvan did. The few times that Rajesh rushed to attend, he returned saying that they have specifically asked for you. The other person was Revanth.

Bhuvan got sick of attending to calls. He never understood why the seniors specifically called him especially when Rajesh took the call.

Once again, the role of duty boys started in the senior house. Also, the 9th class boys became the Tea boys. They brought the Tea kettle post games. Bhuvan and I partnered as Tea boys.

Tea time drove everyone crazy, especially in the senior houses. It reminded me of the desert travelers in search of an oasis.

The tea-boys of Gupta House had a huge challenge of safeguarding our tea from the Pirates of both the Chalukya and the Moghul houses which fell en route from the mess to Gupta House.

There were many tea addicts in 11th & 12th grades. They carried a bottle full of tea and sipped it at regular intervals.

In dramatics, the Moghul house staged a parody on Tea: Once it so happened that one of the tea lovers had to travel across the mountains and valleys across the country in search of a good tea but could find it nowhere. He was fatigued by travel and disappointment. Just then a small boy wearing the Saikorian uniform serves him a cup of tea, which turned out to be the best cup of Tea. He is completely bowled over and asks, *"Which tea is it?"* The kid replies, SAIKOR TEA. The entire auditorium echoed with applause. The Tea served on the next day is still remembered as the best Tea to date.

The quarterly exams were nearing. Few of our seniors started getting telegrams stating, Grandfather serious, come home immediately or Father not keeping well, come home immediately or Granny expired, come home immediately. The 9th graders had managed to score a good aggregate till class 8th. Though none of us planned to fail there was no way we could pass. Exams and studies were last on our minds. I had scored a decent 90%

aggregate in class 6th, which declined to 75-80% in the 8th grade. I was a class topper in English in class 6th. But now the situation was different; forget scoring, even getting passing marks seemed difficult.

If I fail to pass, it would be my first failure in academics. I couldn't accept this failure at any cost. There had to be a way out. I have never copied before, but this time I had to find a way. I couldn't disappoint my parents by failing.

Weighing all other options, I decided to carry an additional sheet inside the examination hall. I arranged it on the back inside my shirt. I had a science paper that day. I entered the exam hall. Tokada was the invigilator. I didn't know how to react. Tokada was extremely strict. I went through the question paper twice. Maybe thrice, but I didn't know the answers. I wasn't even sure whether I could use the paper resting inside my shirt. I felt increasingly restless. I feared failure as well as getting caught.

Between parental disappointment and disciplinary action, I was caught between the devil and the deep sea. Tokada was now suspicious and gave me a keen look. I hated to fail. I slowly began loosening my shirt to pull out the paper. Tokada was now walking horizontally in front of the class and was viewing me from every angle. I managed to pull out my copy sheet and put it inside the main answer sheet. I had just managed to scribble inside my answer sheet.

However, I was totally inexperienced at this. After I managed to put my copy sheet inside the main sheet my heart started pounding. The stress was evident. Tokada understood that something fishy was happening but was not sure what. He got the impression that I was waiting for some answer sheet from someone in the exam hall.

Nevertheless, I couldn't muster enough courage to copy from the material I had with me. The bell rang indicating the end of exam hours.

The next thing I knew was Tokada rushed to my desk and snatched my answer sheet. I had succeeded in making eye contact with Virat who knew what was happening. While I took the answer sheet from Tokada in the guise of tying the additional sheets, Virat stood right in front of me shielding me from Tokada's gaze. Virat was submitting his answer sheets.

Tokada went to collect answer sheets from others. I dropped my copy material down and at the same time Virat dropped his question paper in the guise of picking up his question paper, he gathered my copy material and quickly walked away.

Thank God!

A very relieved me walked out of the class.

As I stepped out, I realized that there is no point in getting so anxious about exams. The results were announced and most of the students from senior house - 9th class had failed. We didn't worry about our scores as much as our parents' reaction to our performance.

Is there a way out? Yes indeed! Our class teachers gave us our progress reports to write the postal addresses of our homes. This was the best opportunity we got. None of our progress reports went to the correct addresses! My report went to Suri's home. Suri's report to mine. It relieved us from the severe scolding we deserved and when our parents enquired, we all simply explained that a new admin has mixed up the addresses and that we have scored 75% or 80% marks as usual.

Post-lunch we were assigned chores by the seniors. We had to go to the cobbler, laundry, tailor, tuck shop, or to other houses. Of all these going to Gajapati house was a nightmare. It was a house filled with different characters. They seemed to have no soul. It was like the Bermuda triangle; dark, mysterious, and dangerous. The 9th and 10th of the Gajapati house used to go to hide in the temple, laundry, and any such place that they couldn't be traced.

Their plight was pitiable. There was no day that they were not beaten up by their seniors, and that too for the craziest possible reasons.

Few were worse than Oil Raja (who used to beg for oil). They had to beg for everything – toothpaste, brush, oil, shoes, polish, socks, clothes. Practically everything.

While getting my shoes mended at a cobbler, I met Sekhar, a 9th grade Gajapatian. Sekhar was tall, dark, and soft-spoken by nature.

"What brings you here, Sekhar? I asked. *"You are supposed to be hiding in the temple by this time."*

"I was caught en route to the temple. I am here to get Manoj's shoes."

Manoj was an 11th grader who was short, muscular, a very good footballer and athlete.

"Manoj! How is he as a person?"

"In Gajapati house there are no persons. There are beasts and Manoj is a moody and unpredictable beast."

Gajapatian seniors were known to be extremely mean.

I smiled. *"They often call 9th class guys but you guys are often into hiding."*

"No matter how hard we try, it's no use. We stay in the same house so there is no escape. Hiding is a temporary relief."

I felt sorry for him.

"By the way Sekhar, your shoelace looks like they are torn out of a bedsheet."

"Hahaha! Oh Yes. But you haven't yet seen the sole of my shoe, have you?" He asked.

"No, no. I haven't," I replied.

"Look at this!"

I was stunned. His shoe had practically no sole left.

"WTF is this Sekhar?"

"Thank God! at least I have these. Some don't even have this. Few are wearing Disco shoes." lamented Sekhar.

"What are Disco shoes?"

"Wearing shoes of different pairs, sometimes different colours, sometimes we are left with two shoes of the same foot."

"So, what happened with your new shoes?"

He laughed; *"You can guess where our shoes have gone."*

"That's horrible!"

Back at the Gupta House, demands from the seniors were limited. The understanding between the 9th and 11th was very cordial. Eventually, Suresh (Suri) went on to become the cadet of RamMohan. I was included in every party thanks to my quick wit and easy nature. I had several bosses in grades 11 and 12.

Mahi (my boss) was my favorite with whom I spent most of my time. He was short and smart and an all-rounder at sports. He was a huge fan of south star Nagarjuna popularly known as Nag.

Life went well for us, till the most notorious boy from class 12th was shifted to the Gupta house. He had created terror among all the juniors in the Moghul house. Vikram was tall, well built, fair, and handsome. He joined the school in the 9th grade and was deliberately put in Gupta House by the administration as the Moghul housemaster couldn't control him. The Gupta housemaster was Mr. Shankar, was popularly known as Gundu for his bald head; a name he hated. Being an ex-Saikorian himself, he treated everybody as his juniors when it came to commanding authority over the students of classes 11 and 12.

Vikram spoke less but when he ordered something, each word had to be attended to with utmost precision. In case of any deviation, the repercussions were evident on our faces for the next two days at least. On a fateful day, at around 6:45 am, Vikram was going to his dormitory after a shower and I crossed his path while entering my dormitory. As I walked to my bed, I heard my name.

"Rambo."

I quickly turned around to look but saw no one. So, I left the call unattended. Then within a second, another call came in a very cold tone, *"You bastard, Rambo."*

That was it. In no time I rushed to Vikram. But he gave me a deadly blow. I couldn't understand what happened. He said nothing and walked away. I went to my dorm. The scar on my cheek was bright red.

Mahi noticed it during lunch and asked *"Are you the first prey of Vikram?"*

"Yes, Boss."

"Good! Let's celebrate by watching a new movie of Nag. Let's bunk school and go to Vizianagaram post-lunch."

"Sure, Boss, I'm all game. You will miss your bottle of tea this evening."

"I'll adjust with a single cup of tea at Vizianagaram," laughed Mahi. *"Don't worry about that!"*

Bunking had rules. Firstly, it has to be done keeping in mind the Duty Master. An alternate adjustment or backup was put in place so that the attendance is tallied during all roll-calls taken. If caught and reported the administrative authorities would take those caught to the task.

It was nothing short of an adventure ride. Luckily on that day, everything was managed with ease. After enjoying the movie, Mahi brought a bottle of Priya Mango Pickle to prepare for a post-dinner pickle party.

The dinner served on Tuesdays, Thursdays, and Fridays in the mess were not good. So, at night we had Pickle Parties.

For Pickle Parties, we covertly transferred all the left-over rice during dinner into a plastic carry bag. Then it was carefully carried from the mess into the house. The rice was then spread over a newspaper kept on the bed and pickle was mixed into the rice and then topped by homemade ghee[12] brought by students after vacations. This was feasted by about 15-20 of us sitting in a circle. The happiness from such dinners was unmatched and unparalleled. The joy ran deep down our hearts. If one hasn't savored that rice, then he had missed out on a delightful flavor of hostel life.

---

12. Ghee – clarified butter made from cows' milk

One day the seniors assigned Suresh and me the task of making arrangements for shoes, toothpaste, soaps, and polish. While carrying out these tasks the house captains of junior houses ensured that no one went to either washrooms or dormitories. The robbery was planned between 6:00-8:00 pm during study hours. At times, close friends of senior house boys in the junior houses did the job and simply handed over the stuff to them. In other cases, like now, the robbery is a daylight adventure. Pradeep the house captain of the Pallava House and my friend from the Crash Program used the timetable of Bampu. The robbery was planned based on this.

It was planned like professional crime. It was only during such a robbery, we realized that during our junior house days, none of our things were actually misplaced. We were simply robbed.

Suresh and I worked hand-in-glove as partners in crime. It was around 10:30 am when we reached the Pallava house. We scanned in and around the house to ensure that there is no staff around. Then Suri slowly got hold of the window shade and managed to jump over the wall into the House. I stood outside as a sentry to keep him updated about the movements outside.

Suri slowly hopped into the house and filled in the sack, with items listed in the order given to us. As he rushed back with his bag, he was confronted with a class 6 boy. Suri was surprised to find him there, but that 6th grader was so shocked that he just stood staring.

Suri pointed a finger at him and shouted, *"Just fuck off from here."*

The boy was terrified and vanished in no time.

He signed me for a clearance signal. I responded. Suri threw the loaded sack over the wall. The sack was not tied and the contents were scattered everywhere. Suri then sent me a surprise package that wasn't on the list and was unexpected. A cricket bat came like a flying saucer and landed straight on my knee. By the time Suri managed to jump over the wall, I was squatting on the ground holding my knee.

"WTF happened?" asked Suri.

"The bat which you just threw, you idiot! Oh, God!! Now hold me along with the stuff and let's walk back to our house."

We had learnt to play with fire. The lines between good, bad and evil were blurring very fast. But this was no time to ponder over such trivial stuff.

One day Sekhar from Gajapati house came asking for me. When I heard this, I trembled with fear.

"Why the fuck would someone personally come to call me?"

"It's not someone. It's Manoj," cautioned Sekhar

"Oh, God! What the hell has he got to do with me?"

"No idea!"

I informed Mahi before leaving to meet Manoj of Gajapati House.

"Don't you worry Rambo just go and if there is any problem, I am here," assured Mahi.

"Ok, Boss."

As I entered the Gajapati house, I saw Dhanu, Arjun, and Ramesh (all my classmates of 9th from Gajapati) running around with no trace of life on their faces. Every second passed was a miserable memory for them.

"There's Manoj," Sekhar pointed.

I ran up to Manoj, *"Boss, did you call me."*

"Who the hell are you, man?"

"Boss, I am Rambo from the Gupta House."

Manoj laughed out loud. *"So, you are the Rambo. Your Guptans keep telling us stories about you that – you are this and that and does this and that."*

"I imagined that you must be quite a giant-like personality, but you look like a bloody skeleton, man. Why the hell do they call you Rambo- for God's sake?"

I narrated the story behind my name.

"Sounds interesting; anyways let me see what Rambo's body looks like. Take off your shirt and stand against the wall."

In no time I stood against the wall. *"Okay, I think I have seen you enough now. Fuck off."* Manoj dismissed me. I vanished from there in no time.

For the 9th graders of Gajapati house life was changing from bad to worse.

When the new joinees (who joined in class 9th) were bullied by their classmates in their class 11, they began venting their frustrations on our hapless classmates of Gajapati house. Gajapati house was a mess. It appeared as if all the specimens of their batch were put together in one house.

Varun wanted to be fanned, though the fan was on. Rohan wanted Colgate toothpaste, Parachute coconut oil, and Lux soap without paying a penny. Most of the time the 9th graders contributed money from their meager pocket money to meet such demands of seniors. For their own use, they began stealing used soaps from junior houses and share these for bathing. They conned the tuck shop owner by diverting his attention and stealing whatever was possible.

Though they felt ashamed of their actions they had no choice. Getting slapped was the new normal. Whenever their seniors wanted entertainment, they invented new methods of pleasure-seeking punishments. In the process they invented a water slap i.e., they used to slap the juniors by filling their palms with water. It caused unbearable pain and their cheeks would swell up for days. All that they needed was a scapegoat; never a reason.

The crisis soon escalated to a feeling of emergency. We, the 9th graders of senior houses hatched a plan to end our trauma. We planned to send a message to our administration about our plight. It had to be discreet. As part of the plan, we decided to let two boys who lived close by, escape from school and reach their homes. Thus, Sekhar from Gajapati house and Bhuvan from the Gupta house who were from Visakhapatnam (about 120 km away from the school) left school and reached their homes. After they left, the 9th graders created a ruckus to bring the matter to light.

The school administration was forced to adopt damage control measures to save the reputation of the school. They requested the parents of both children to bring them. They assured that they would ensure no such incidents of harassment by the seniors will be repeated in the future.

For the first time in the history of the school, a major change was made.

In order to keep up their promise, the school administration decided to shift back all the 9th class students to their respective junior houses with immediate effect. This was an out of the box decision made by the administration.

Our motive behind sending this message to the administration was to make them understand our plight and put a monitoring mechanism in place so that we wouldn't be in such a pitiable state. We hadn't expected this and were supremely happy. Though we were on cloud nine, we pretended to be sorry before our bosses. I insisted that my Boss should not worry about tea and that I would serve him tea daily. He laughed it off saying, *"You bastard, now it's time for you to get your tea served. Don't worry about me. I'll take care of myself".*

In order to accommodate us in junior houses, our double bunk beds were shifted to junior houses. It was now confirmed that we would be living in the junior houses. A feeling of helpless, wordless displeasure washed over the junior houses including the Housemaster Bampu.

Chapter **9**	**Class IX**
	Part II – A Twist in the Tale

It was a critical time in the history of the school. The effect of the students' insurgence had a comprehensive effect. The incident created ripples across all sections and resulted in a sweeping wave of changes that affected all.

The school felt that they had taken the best corrective and preventive measures. They could face parents of the 9th graders of the senior house, especially those of Bhuvan and Sekhar, confidently. An implicit message, loud and clear had gone to the seniors that the administration is effective in dealing with any situation. It also was an inferred warning against bullying.

The change was a shocker for the seniors. They could not digest the action taken; particularly, seniors of Gajapati House. They were furious at the 9th graders for rebelling. They felt helpless but were sure that merely changing houses will not disconnect them from established connections. They were confident that, no matter what happened, as seniors, they could still boss around.

The housemasters of the junior houses were flummoxed too. They felt that students who had returned would not obey them. The boys would be uncontrollable as they were exposed to senior houses. They also had to deal with resentment the students might bear for sending them to senior houses.

The new joinees in the 9th grade were disturbed. They felt that their new mates have lived with intense bullying and torture. What if they turned against them? They sensed deep distrust, despair, and fear. The 9th graders who had progressed from 6th grade were in the school for three years and hence considered themselves seniors to the new joinees in 9th grade. The new joinees didn't have any hope of building trust and amicable relations with them any time soon. They were afraid of the humiliation and indignity they could face.

The 9th graders from the junior house held mixed feelings. They were happy to welcome their classmates back but they were aware of their past experience in senior houses. They felt their pain but were suspicious of them as they felt that they may have changed emotionally and there could be a possibility of a backlash. They had memories of fun times they had shared but were nervous too.

For the other juniors of the junior house like class 8, it hardly made a difference. They were happy in a way that they could hear the experiences of being in senior house. They are also skeptical because with the arrival of senior house 9th class, the might of class 9 as a whole would increase manifold and they might be taken to task by their Prefects at the behest of 9th graders from senior house.

For 6th and 7th graders it mattered a lot. They were terrified to hear the news. Their voices shook while even speaking in whispers. They trembled as they had never even raised their heads to look up at the students from the senior houses. They were clearly anxious.

For us, the 9th graders who were returning from the senior house, it felt like a homecoming. We had lived a dark phase and now it was the time to take a break and rejoice. All we could think of was our new found freedom.

We felt that we were born again. Not to mention the confidence of having the support of our bosses from the senior houses in case of need.

We arrived. Bag and baggage. It was a joyous moment. We were relieved. We were home, back in Pallava House.

Bampu, entered the dormitory in his bare-chested avatar on hearing cheering and shouting by class 9th students.

"Kick you bloody fellow, Ring leader, RamaKrishna," he roared.

Everybody burst out in laughter.

"This is what I missed the most in senior house Sir," I replied.

"Now that you are back from senior house doesn't mean you behave like seniors," declared Bampu.

"Okay!" everybody giggled.

Bampu sensed the excitement and happiness when he had just walked into the room; he left, leaving us to ourselves.

After a long break, we, the 9th graders from the Pallava House picked up our cricket kit and moved to the ground by 3:00 pm and played like we had done earlier, before going to senior houses.

The atmosphere of the junior houses had changed on our return. The casual attitude we had at senior house turned out to be contagious and affected the rest of the class. Nobody gave a damn about anything. The slackness towards studies, activities, discipline and in everything else showed up everywhere and other boys began emulating it. It seemed harmless fun. Nobody cared about the Housemaster Bampu's instructions or what House Tutors taught. Very soon and surely, control of junior houses was taken over by those who had returned from the senior houses. Days passed.

Each house had two tutors – working in shifts - during study hours - between 6:00 to 8:00 pm. The study hours began at 6:00 pm. It was 6:30 pm already. The 9th graders were still taking their baths. Mr. RaviKumar, who had joined the school only recently was the Tutor for the day. He was short and stout, very strict, and had a temper to match.

He became restless when the 9th graders, particularly those who returned from the senior house, didn't turn up at the study hall. He shouted out to the 9th graders from the study hall. His voice echoed through the silent hallway leading to the dormitory. Nobody responded. He was getting madder by the minute. The students seated in the hall were smiling among themselves. RaviKumar noticed and got livid.

He came up to the entrance of our dormitory and stood there.

"*Inside.*"

Few boys who were ready and dressed walked past him nonchalantly. He yelled furiously at them. They quietly walked to the study hall. He warned everyone inside the dormitory to be present inside the study hall within the next five minutes and turned to go back to the study. Suresh, Virat, and I had just finished our bath. We came out of the bathroom wearing towels to see what the noise was about. Seeing us, RaviKumar lost his cool.

"*You bloody fools! Don't you have manners?*" He yelled

"*What do you want, Sir? Why are you yelling?*" I replied boldly and rudely, placing one hand over my hip and setting my still wet hair with the other hand.

Suresh and Virat laughed out loud.

RaviKumar felt insulted.

He instantly slapped me. "*You idiot,*" he yelled.

I was shocked and so were Suri and Virat.

I touched my cheek, closed my eyes, and was about to lose my temper.

Suri held my hand from behind and whispered, "*Stay calm. We will see him later.*"

I spoke very coldly to RaviKumar, "*You may go, Sir. We will reach the study hall shortly.*"

RaviKumar was shaken by the episode. He had rarely slapped a student before. It was not intentional. He walked back to the study hall. Suri, Virat and I went back to the bathroom. We reached the study hall around 7:00

pm and again regarded RaviKumar with a cold look. In a few minutes, the whole class learned about the incident. Our classmates felt hurt and angry at what happened.

The study hall had gone quiet and dense with emotion. Anger. Hurt. Indignation. All waited for the clock to strike at 8:00 pm.

Dinner time.

Time has its own pace. Second after second. It never goes slow. It never races. Just because we are in a hurry and desperate to get away from the situation, time doesn't fly.

We have to hold on to our nerves to deal with any situation. Time doesn't hurry.

RaviKumar and I kept looking at each other's faces angrily.

The siren rang. The wave of anger between us, broke, and like others, we moved towards the mess.

My classmates in the last row were upset.

"How dare he touch Rambo?" raged Rajesh.

"I think we need to show him his place," suggested Manohar.

"What does he think of himself?" rallied Bhuvan.

"Let us show him, what we can," droned Revanth.

"Yes," everybody echoed in unison, *"he shouldn't be spared."*

RaviKumar felt dagger eyes boring into him. He sensed that hitting me impulsively didn't go down well with my classmates. But the damage was done.

During dinner as my classmates discussed this incident, I went up to my bosses from class 11th and 12th of the Gupta House and informed them about the tutor RaviKumar slapping me.

"How dare he touch our Rambo?"

"That too, RaviKumar? He has been in the school just over a year and he has done the unthinkable!"

RaviKumar entered the mess for dinner.

"Hahahaha, what a coincidence, I thought he wouldn't be turning up for dinner to mess tonight," laughed Boss Mahi.

"Just relax. We will deal with him." I puffed up with pride, and returned to join my friends for dinner.

Seeing my confidence, and arrogance they understood that soon the tables will turn around.

RaviKumar was observing me and my friends. He began feeling uncomfortable. *"What the hell is going on here? What are they plotting? I shouldn't have come to mess for dinner now."*

The school captain, Master C.H.V. Sudhakar from Chalukya House banged the dining table once. The dining hour concluded with a prayer. Those who were still eating began gulping down their food. The others dispersed to their houses.

I and my friends were still seated. We watched as 11th and 12th graders of Gupta House walked towards RaviKumar's table. A startled RaviKumar was circled by 30-35 strong and well-built muscular senior house boys led by Rupesh, RamMohan, and Mahi. RaviKumar couldn't say anything. The gang warned, *"Sir, you may be new and not well versed with the ground realities of the school. Better you behave yourself; else we have to teach you how to behave."* RaviKumar was quiet all the while.

Unfortunately for him, on that day, not many teachers were in the mess. The ones who were present were junior teachers who didn't wish to meddle. RaviKumar understood clearly the reason behind the adamant attitude of the senior house 9th class students and me in particular. All that RaviKumar could say to the seniors was one word. *"Sorry."*

He had gone pale. After all the seniors left, I and my friends were still sitting there to gloat over our victory. RaviKumar was embarrassed when he looked at us holding our heads high and staring at him with arrogance. We nodded our heads at him to show pity. RaviKumar sunk in shame and walked out of the mess.

The story of this incident spread. It smelt pure victory. It conveyed a message to my classmates that we have a strong backing of the senior houses. It also showed that though the seniors terrorized and used us, they also took care of us. After this, we became more adamant, arrogant, and egoistic. The housemasters were totally undermined.

It was gala time for us in the junior houses. We were the undisputed kings. We found our lost freedom and started spending time in fun. We introduced the pickle-rice buffet system in the junior houses.

One day, during classes P.S.K. Verma of the 9th grade and Ravikanth who was a new joinee in the 9th grade of the Maurya House were sitting behind Pradeep. For no apparent reason, they scribbled his nickname (Hippo) on the back of his uniform. Pradeep was the Pallava house captain. He was looked up with respect by the juniors of the house. He had earned this admiration. One could play around with him, as a friend in an individual capacity, but they should have taken his position seriously. But these two didn't think that far and scribbled on his uniform.

Pradeep realized that something was being scribbled on his back. The harm was done by then. Pradeep had to go to his house to change his shirt. If a junior saw his shirt, he would become the butt of all jokes. He was proud of his position and uniform. Pradeep left for his dormitory immediately to change. The Pallavans were on the way to the mess for their lunch, and the scribbling issue became the hot topic.

"How dare they do it?" we thought.

Post-lunch, we returned to our houses. From our washroom area, we could see each other through windows. Our houses were twenty meters away. An argument erupted between my class (9th-grade Pallavans) and the Mauryans. The matter escalated to an extent that Pallavans challenged the Mauryans to physical combat. We were very strong and began provoking them. We wanted to teach each Mauryan a lesson for what they had done to Pradeep. The Mauryans didn't stand a chance.

The Mauryans weighed their chances position in case of a physical tussle. They came up with an alternative; only the boys involved in the issue would fight it out instead of the entire class.

We asked the Mauryans to hand over the two culprits to take them to the task. The Mauryans knew that the boys would be beaten to a pulp if handed over to the entire class. They insisted that the duel should be between the three boys only, i.e., Pradeep vs Verma and Ravikant.

Pradeep was strong, brave, and confident. He was hefty and now full of rage. Verma was tall with a delicate body and a running nose. Ravikanth was short and wore specs. He had recently joined the school in the 9th grade and was frightened at the sudden turn of events. Ravikanth had not expected the prank to boomerang so badly. Pradeep was okay with the deal. They were looking for the right place for the duel.

It was decided to battle on the ground. The 9th graders from both houses left for the ground. Angry words flew between the two houses - from their windows. The argument was heard by many.

The day was Sunday.

At 3.30 pm.

It was hot and sunny outside.

The Pallavans wanted to use the opportunity to bash up every Mauryan. The Mauryans were happy for being able to broker this deal and felt victorious because of the 1:2 ratios.

We, Pallavans wore our green sports t-shirts. Mauryans wore their red sports t-shirts. We finally met in the farthest football court on the ground, where usually we played cricket. Today the playground had turned into a battlefield.

The only rule was that, both the Mauryans can't attack the Pallavan at the same time. The lines for the duel were drawn. It was called, 'The Battle of the Brave Hearts'. Pallavans and Mauryans were standing behind their respective warriors and cheering. Pradeep seemed like Mohammed Ali during his prime years. All he wanted was a chance to knock them down with a single blow, right from the moment they scribbled on his back.

Both the Mauryans looked pessimistic. They neither had the courage to face Pradeep nor the guts to challenge him. But by looking at the crowd cheering for them, they didn't run away from the battle.

"Come on Pradeep, all you need is two blows," shouted the Pallavans.

"Yes. Just two blows to knock down these bastards," yelled Pradeep.

None of the two Mauryans were ready to take a single step forward. Eventually, they were pushed from behind by their housemates.

"It's a matter of pride for us, you are two. Just push yourselves," cheered the Mauryans from behind.

No amount of cheering helped. They knew they would be easily bashed up.

With great reluctance, Verma stepped ahead. He had to show some courage. The Pallavans booed him and he took two steps backward. *Pride was not important. Life was.* Fear took over both the Mauryans. Pradeep had to move towards them as they were retreating. Verma escaped from the first blow of Pradeep and he ran behind Pradeep to hold him from behind. Pradeep was so annoyed with Verma's escape that he pushed Verma with all his might. Verma fell flat on the ground. Ravikanth rushed to Pradeep. Pradeep looked furiously at him. RaviKanth stood stunned.

"You little bastard, I'll show you what I am." He squeezed RaviKanth's hand and gave him a blow on his shoulder.

RaviKanth's eyes blurred with tears.

Meanwhile, Verma managed to stand and was holding his fist covering his face. Pradeep quickly managed to bash him through his fists onto his face.

Verma could feel the blood from his lips.

RaviKanth tried to reach out to Pradeep again; this time Pradeep held RaviKanth by his neck and this rendered him breathless for a while.

Pradeep spared him when he pleaded.

Pallavans were still cheering for Pradeep.

Meanwhile, both the Mauryans pleaded with him to stop. Pradeep, who was now tired of battling them one after the other and felt that they have got their lesson for what they have done. Finally, everyone called for a truce.

Just then a 7th class guy from the Maurya House came running towards us.

It was time for sports. The 9th class guys began running to the fall-in line in the arena for roll-call before the start of games.

Many of us failed to notice that, apart from Mr. RaviKumar, who was the Duty Master that day, Pavan, the housemaster of the Maurya House was standing there. He was a strict mathematics teacher and never tolerated nonsense. He could terrorize the students with just his bearing and harsh tone. He trashed boys when he thought they needed disciplining. He was feared. Pavan was closely looking at the 9th class boys. He knew that what was going on was not a game. It was a fight. The Mauryan 8th graders had let it slip out that 'The Battle of the Brave Hearts', was a battle. He alerted the staff and mobilized them to the ground.

It was about 4:15 pm. The Mauryan housemaster walked up to Goyal, the house captain of the Maurya House and asked him in a very harsh tone,

"What are you doing on the ground? Why have you come early? Why didn't you inform me?"

The Mauryan captain replied innocently, "We came to play cricket with the Pallavans Sir."

"I see," observed Mr. Pavan.

"Is that how Verma and Ravikanth are hurt? Their faces are bruised."

The house captain didn't reply.

Then he walked up to RaviKanth and asked harshly. *"Do you play cricket? I have never seen you. Tell me the truth; else I'm not going to spare you."*

Then he walked up to Verma and hissed, *"It's good that you started playing cricket. It's better late than never."*

The group was quiet. Teachers began surrounding the Pallavan and Mauryan 9th graders. Some didn't know what was going on. The senior house students too, didn't know of the duel. Discrete inquiries were made and the story of the battle spread. The teachers had to take action.

We were agitated. *"What do these teachers have to do with our fight? What is Mr. Pavan up to? Why is he trying to show off now?"*

RaviKumar was the Duty Master for the day and the House Tutor of the Pallava House. He wanted to use the opportunity to get back at us.

He went up to Pradeep. *"What happened? What is the problem? Are the Pallavans involved in this? Since your housemaster isn't present, I represent your House today. Now tell me?"*

We were right behind. *"How fast people forget what happened with them,"* someone taunted. The rest of us giggled.

RaviKumar heard it but kept his cool. He fired Pradeep. *"I'm asking you Pradeep. Why don't you respond?"* His frustration was visible.

Mr. Pavan held RaviKanth by his collar and pulled him out of the file. *"Tell me what happened else you will get the time of your life,"* he warned.

Other teachers also began raising their voices. *"We know everything. Give us the names."* Nobody said a word.

This silence from us, hurt their ego and they became more aggressive. Mr. Reddy and Mr. Rao joined in.

Mr. Reddy, our physical trainer was tall, dark, and heavy. Mr. Rao sported a physically fit body and a bald pate. He was very disciplined and cycled all the time though he owned a scooter. He used to check the shoes of the seniors every Monday and hence was indirectly responsible for the juniors washing the canvas shoes of their seniors, He was rumored to be powerful and in close contact with the headmaster and the principal. The seniors left him alone.

Class 9th of both the Pallava and the Maurya Houses were taken to task. RaviKumar was taking the roll-call of all the houses before games. Still rankled by our comments, he was in a state of continuous irritation.

During the roll-call of Pandya house, he noticed the boys talking and shouted at the 9th-grade Pandyans, *"You idiots, don't you have any bloody common sense? Behave yourselves."* This irked them. *"Ravi is simply too much,"* they gossiped.

When RaviKumar was walking away from them after the roll-call, Vineel an old 9th grader from Pandya house pelted a small pebble in his direction. Unfortunately, it landed on RaviKumar's head. Vineel rolled his eyes in astonishment. Never in his life had he hit a target, inspite of being a member of the shooting club. It had hit the target now; but to his chagrin, the wrong person, wrong time and wrong place.

RaviKumar turned to look at them. He not only felt humiliated, but harassed. He couldn't take it anymore and rushed towards class 9th students. *"Who did it? I want to know."*

The teachers around knew that something was wrong. They rushed to him and enquired, *"What happened?"*

"These 9th class rascals threw a stone on me." He shouted.

That was it. It was like the last nail in the coffin.

The school captain announced all others to disperse for the games as he too had to be there. Vineel had taken everyone by surprise. His classmates Deepak, Yagna, Dinesh, and Sudha looked exasperatedly at him. *"Why Vineel?"*

"It just happened. As a reflex," he replied.

The incident not only added fuel to fire, It became a huge raging fire. The teachers were enraged and they singled out our class.

The question was, *"Who threw the stone?"*

No answer.

Silence.

This made the teachers angrier.

"There is no point in asking these idiots." It was Tokada. *"They only deserve to be bashed."* Saying this he used a cane and began caning us like farmers thrash paddy. Other teachers joined in.

Including RaviKumar.

Along with the Mauryan housemaster.

It was a direct attack on the teacher's self-respect and dignity.

The teachers made us run for twenty tracks, gave us physically straining exercises and exhaustive punishments for over an hour and a half. But no answers came.

This incident made the teachers feel helpless. All they got in reply to their questions was a haunting smile. So, they went to Mr. Rao for advice. Mr. Rao felt sorry for the teachers. He said that these boys have now become thick-skinned on account of their exposure to the senior houses. *"No amount of punishment by us can change them. They shouldn't be left like this in the open; rather they should be put back into their cages."* Mr. Pavan and RaviKumar agreed.

Mr. Rao then had a meeting with the principal and the headmaster and revealed to them all that had happened. Dealing with the 9th graders - especially with those who had returned from the senior houses, had become a daunting task. Their homecoming had resulted in a new challenge. The 9th graders of the junior house had also turned into rebels. Very soon the entire 9th grade will go out of hand. *"Timely and effective action is needed,* he warned them. *The junior housemasters and tutors are losing their morale in dealing with these idiots,"* said Mr. Rao agitatedly.

They realized that the 9th students can be handled only by the seniors. So, sending them back to senior houses would be the ultimate remedy. *"But since they are used to their seniors by now, their houses should be shuffled,"* advised headmaster.

The headmaster was an ex-Saikorian. He was physically fit, smart and alert. He was good at sports too and often played hockey with the seniors. Due to his diminutive stature, he was nick-named Mr. Sparrow.

Our principal had a big wart on his face sported a large mustache, hence was called Daku. He had a slightly receding hairline which was fast turning white.

The juniors wanted to be in his good books as he had a beautiful young daughter. Daku couldn't agree more with Sparrow. They decided to randomly shuffle those who came from senior houses while sending them back to senior houses.

Revanth, Vamshi, and I were marked for Chalukya House. Rajesh, Manohar, and Bhuvan - to Gajapati House. Suri and Virat were lucky and were retained in Gupta House. All the senior house 9th students were reshuffled to different houses. The idea of master-mind Sparrow was to create an identity crisis for all 9th graders returned from senior house by ensuring that we feel lost in a new setting by losing the powerful contacts that we built so far. He was quite sure that after this reshuffling class 9 can be controlled. In this process, Pradeep who was identified as a rebel was moved to the Moghul House. Verma to Chalukya House. However, RaviKanth was left in Maurya House as his health was delicate. He was given a stern warning.

As expected by Sparrow, the new changes sent a shock wave among all the 9th class students. Nobody ever imagined that such a small instance of scribbling could finally lead to such a catastrophic effect and cost them their precious freedom. It was like living a nightmare.

It was all plain clear now. Their wellbeing depended on how well their bosses from their erstwhile Houses connected to the new houses. Luckily for me, my boss - Mahi had amazing friends from the Chalukya House. So, I assured Revanth and Vamshi that they can smoothly make their in-roads into the Chalukya House. Likewise, everybody made their own connections. But the most disheartening part was that these networking and interpersonal connections had no effect on the Gajapatians. Bhuvan wept after he was told of his new house. So did the others who moved to the Gajapati House. For Sekhar, it was a relief. He had borne the brunt of the Gajapati house. He now belonged to the Chalukya House. There were hardly 45 days left for the academic year to end.

Finally, the entire 9th grade moved to their allocated houses. Now every senior house had students from all the four junior houses, except for the Chalukya House. All the erstwhile senior house Chalukyans were reshuffled to other houses. The Chalukya house looked as if, all the pale candidates in sports were handpicked and put in the same basket. None of us were good at sports. We were average to below-average in all activities. The Chalukyans had the tradition of winning the Cross-Country trophy over the past few years. Winning the trophy was a matter of prestige. Cross-country is a 12 kilometers race for the senior students and 8 kilometers race for the juniors.

On our arrival to the Chalukya House, we were immediately called for a fall-in, at the kabaddi court by the class 11 students. As it was during the fag end of the academic year, both the class 10 and 12 students were very busy with their preparation for the board exams. The fall-in was presided by Amarender (Amar) and MadhuBabu who were tall and athletic. Later RajaRao, Kumar, Ravishankar Naik (Naik) and Raghuvardhan joined them. Kumar and RajaRao were short and muscular. Naik was physically fit but cranky. Raghuvardhan, the mess vice-captain, was an accomplished shooter and was plumpy.

Amarender addressed the house. *"I think you guys know that Chalukya House is known for winning the cross-country trophy. But looking at you guys we feel that you are all hopeless. Is that so?"* asked Amarender.

"No, Boss," all responded.

"That's good. That's the spirit. We understand your capabilities and weaknesses. Don't worry about them. We will take, what is required out of you. Are you ready to give?"

"Yes, Boss," shouted out all the class 9th students.

"Good," observed RajaRao.

"So, who are all here and from which house?" asked Kumar.

"Boss, three of us; myself, Revanth and Vamshi are from Gupta."

"Aditya, Srikanth and Sanjeev are from Moghul."

"Sekhar, Dhanu, Arjun and Verma are from Gajapati House, Boss," I continued.

"Surprisingly, we have got members from all the junior houses except from our own Pandya house" laughed Kumar. *"Anyways welcome to all of you."*

"This is a different house with a different set of ethos, so you better understand it and behave accordingly. Learn to be like a Roman in Rome, okay!" directed Raghuvardhan.

"Sure, Boss," we replied in unison and dispersed.

Everyone and everything were new to us. We didn't know anybody in person till then.

Though the number of days we spent with the class 12 Chals were few, we did share some memorable moments with them. I became a caddie of 2-3 class 12 students from Chalukya House, due to my tongue-in-cheek kind of humor. Once, it so happened that I was in the senior dormitory attending Kalyan's (class 12 student) work. All of a sudden, Kalyan's friend showed him the index finger. *"Do you remember this finger?"*

"No."

"How could you forget this finger? Try to remember, I'm asking you about this finger dude, this finger."

Kalyan replied, *"Yeah! Now I remember. This is the one you put in my arse."*

Everybody burst laughing. I bit my tongue to stop laughing.

Kalyan asked me, *"Do you know about that finger?"*

I smiled and answered, *"No, Boss."*

"It's better you don't," commented Kalyan and laughed out loud.

We shared an amicable relationship with class 12 and got to know them better. We also formed a good bonding among ourselves. Adi, Dhanu, and I became thick friends and spent quite a lot of time together. Adi and I chatted late into the night. We were friends right from class 6 when we shared the same bench thanks to Mr. Pavan, our mathematics teacher. He thought I was good at all the subjects except mathematics. So, he made me to sit with Adi. It was like reuniting with a lost friend.

Normally Board exams commence before the regular annual exams. So, class 12 would be the first to leave school, followed by 10th and then the rest. After the completion of their Board exams, class 12 students were given a grand farewell by their housemates and their cadets. The houses hosted a party with dinner, music, dance, and celebration. The farewell was tearful. Everybody wished them well.

As one batch left, a new batch had arrived at the school. Class 11 moved to 12 and faced the stress of board exams. The real joy is for those who stepped into Class 11.

Clearing the exam looked daunting for me and others like me. The big question was: *When we couldn't pass the quarterly and half-yearly exams, how could we expect to pass the annual exams.*

If we didn't pass the annuals we surely will be kicked out of the school.

There was no way we could hide our results from our parents if we failed now. As the annual exams approached Dhanu and I were really worried. It was a matter of 'do or die' for us. We connected well with all our seniors and could manage every critical situation but there seemed no solution for this crisis now.

Adi and Arjun were our only sources of strength. So, we decided to do whatever it took to pass the exam. I studied with Adi, and Dhanu with Arjun. Even the seniors didn't disturb us as they were in the same condition. We studied late and tried to learn whatever we could in the limited time. Adi and Arjun helped us and we tried to cram in as much as possible. We cleverly managed to work in areas whereby we could manage to score at least passing marks. We didn't expect to score beyond 40% but we didn't want to score anything less than 40% either. So, it was hard work indeed.

The same was the case with a majority of the senior house 9th class boys. Everybody was holding on to one or two bright students in their respective houses. The lights of the study hall used to be on till late nights - 3:00 am some days. All of us had slogged to make an entry into the school. Nobody wanted to get themselves kicked out due to failure. Thanks to our die-hard spirit, we put in our heart and soul and did the best possible.

The two most important things awaited us was - the results of class 9 this year and the cross-country next year.

Chapter **10**	**Class X** **Part I – Testing the Troubled** **Waters**

C lass 9 was a hurdle we passed much to our relief.
We were back at School to new changes in the house. The 9th graders who were in the junior houses were assigned senior houses in class 10th. It was a big change for us. Though we were together for the past four years, we had minimal interaction. Not to add, the angst and rivalry on the sports field showed up in all our interactions. We also stood as competitors to the Cock House championship as we belonged to different houses.

We didn't share much bonding. The boys who were left behind in the Pandya House in 9th Grade, mainly good at academics. The new joinees of the Pandya House were also good only at academics.

I now belonged to Chalukya house. Between Pandya and Chalukya houses we had very few boys who were good at sports. This spelt disaster for the Cock House competition and particularly for the Cross-Country race. It was a major cause of concern for everybody. Class 10 of Chalukya House stood nowhere in sports, when compared to the other houses. We still had to perform and win with the available resources.

Few 9th graders had now shifted to Chalukya House as per tradition. We had to face challenges, in a completely new environment. There was a feeling of mutual suspicion and distrust.

A fall-in was called for by Amarender and RajaRao of class 12. We obeyed. This was the first fall-in for the 10th and 9th graders who came from the junior house. The new joinees were anxious, just like we were, on our first fall-in during our class 9th. The fear factor is proportionate to the power of the senior. Amarender and RajaRao were two names we had often heard. We were anxious from the moment we got the summons. Our palms were now wet with perspiration.

We fell silent as they arrived.

"So, you are the guys from the junior house," asked Amar.

"Yes, Master."

"No more Master now. Didn't these buggers tell you?" rebuked RajaRao.

"Boss, even before we could tell them anything you have called us for fall-in."

"I know Rambo. You never have time for anything and have a bloody reason for everything."

Everybody smiled.

Amar continued, *"We know about all of you guys and about your abilities, rather disabilities. But as you know, we have a tradition of winning the cross-country race and in no way, we can afford to lose it; no matter what."*

"Yes, Boss."

RajaRao warned, *"We may spare you for anything, but this, and Rambo, don't even think of giving any bloody fucking excuses."*

"Ok, Boss," I quipped.

"Just remember that we are good, as long as you are doing what is required of you. If we are good, you are okay."

"Yes, Boss," we shouted.

"You may disperse now."

They walked away asking me, Adi and Dhanu to report.

We reported as ordered.

"What have you brought from vacations?"

We gave a list of all that we brought.

"Let's share them over the rooftop tonight then," suggested both Amar and RajaRao.

Post-dinner that night about six boys from grade 12 and the three of us sat on the rooftop of our dormitory and polished off goodies our families had packed for us.

"Who is the one who brings maximum snacks from vacation?" asked Kumar.

"Revanth." Dhanu replied without a second thought.

"Okay. Let's check his cupboard," proposed RajaRao.

"Why don't we ask him, Boss?" I countered.

"It doesn't look good on our part to ask them, the way we can ask you."

"So, what's the alternative, Boss?" asked Adi.

"LOOT it guys," ordered RajaRao.

We waited till it was 11:00 pm.

The three of us got down into the dormitory. Revanth wasn't on his bed. His keys weren't under his pillow. I pulled at the doors of his cupboard. There was a small gap between the doors. I had thin hands. They slid inside easily.

However, the packets were big and I couldn't pull them out.

Meanwhile, Dhanu saw Revanth coming into the dormitory and signaled me to move away. I slid down into my bed.

Revanth had come from the study hall after attending to some senior's work. He flopped on the bed after putting his keys under the pillow.

Then Adi, pretended to come running from the senior dormitory calling out for Revanth. Revanth was tired and sleepy by then.

"What happened Adi?"

"Amar is looking for you, Revanth."

"Oh, God! Why are they after me?" muttered Revanth.

He went running to the senior's dormitory. Dhanu and I opened his cupboard and took all the goodies. We replaced the keys under his pillow and returned to the rooftop. Revanth, searched for Amar everywhere; right from the dormitory, study hall, recreation room, kabaddi court, and even the washrooms before returning to his bed.

He found Adi, who was pretending to be asleep.

"Adi, where is Amar?"

"Don't worry, Revanth. Amar has just left for Gajapati House. I have attended to his work so you may go to sleep," assured Adi.

Revanth thanked him and hit the bed. Slowly Adi pulled himself off the bed and crawled over to the rooftop to join the party.

By 12:00 pm we had polished off Revanth's food. We got down from the rooftop. I arranged the covers of all the containers in Revanth's cupboard by pushing my hand through the door.

The next day post-lunch, Revanth found out almost all his delicious food was stolen. Only a little was left. He was raving angry when I saw him.

"Some bloody buggers have stolen my snacks," he shouted.

"How can that be?" I exclaimed.

"Impossible!" added Adi.

"Why don't you check properly again?" asked Dhanu.

"There is nothing left to check. You guys can see, this is what is left," cried Revanth.

"We feel so sorry for you man, we tried to console him. *You can have our stuff; it's not a big deal."*

"No, thank you," replied a very upset Revanth. *"They have stolen my favorite food prepared by my mother with so much love. Idiots could have asked me; I would have given them."*

We looked at each other's faces not knowing what to say.

"I'm not going to spare the culprits; I am going to report to Amar." Revanth declared as he rushed to the senior dormitory.

He returned with a joyful face. *"Amar has asked all of us to fall-in in the kabaddi court."*

"Oh, God! We are going to have it now," cried everybody and rushed to the kabaddi court.

Both Amar and RajaRao came for the fall-in. Adi, Dhanu, and I were standing in the last file smiling at them.

"You bastards, how can you steal the eatables from your own classmate?" thundered Amar.

"How can you be so irresponsible?" asked RajaRao.

They had the faintest smiles. Only those every close would know.

"Revanth, do you suspect anybody?"

"I am not sure, Boss. But I feel it could be my classmates," drawled Revanth.

"Shame on you, idiots" chided Amar.

"Why are those three in the last file laughing? Have you done it buggers?" asked RajaRao.

Our smiles broadened.

"Boss, we feel sorry for our friend, but we will compensate for his loss," we proposed.

"We are really ashamed, Boss. We are sorry for Revanth and we will share our food with him," I offered.

All others joined in the chorus.

"We are sorry, Revanth."

"Do you want me to take them to the task?" Amar asked Revanth.

Revanth who by now had calmed down sighed *"No, Boss. We will take care, and thank you for your concern."*

"Learn from him, you idiots. There should be no more complaints. This should be the last one. Else you will be taken to task."

"It will be the last one only if you decide, Boss," Dhanu quipped.

"Now disperse you shameless idiots," he ordered.

After everybody dispersed, Adi and Dhanu, and I met Revanth. *"Your snacks may have been really delicious, but never mind, we can share ours. Come on now."*

We met Amar and RajaRao later. *"Boss you almost hinted that we are the culprits."*

"Of course! You are!" laughed Amar.

Just then Ravishankar Naik called me – *"Rambo what was your Token number in the last cross-country?"*

To his surprise I replied, *"I'm sorry, Boss. I don't remember."*

"If this is how you treat the cross-country, we won't win the trophy. Moreover, looks like nobody in class 10th is fit enough to make us champions. Anyways I will shortly call for a fall-in," declared Naik.

Back in our dormitory, I called all the 10th class boys. Pandu, the ex vice-captain of the Pandya house during our class 9th refused to join us. I was surprised.

"What's your problem?" I asked.

Pandu argued, *"Why should I come? Who are you to ask everybody to come and meet you?"*

"What's wrong with it? Do you want all of us to come to your place?" I asked

"No!"

"Then what's your problem?"

"We are all Pandyans. You don't belong to our House and you can't command us," explained Pandu.

"What the fuck is wrong with you man? Are you in your senses?" asked Adi. *"So, what if we don't belong to your house?"*

"Can you take charge of the 10th and balance out with class 12th?" I asked.

Aswani Kumar (ex-captain of the Pandya house) interjected, *"Sorry Rambo, we failed to understand the reality here."*

"No problem, Aswani. We are all here now. It doesn't really matter which junior house we belonged to. Somebody must shoulder the responsibility and represent us to the seniors and other houses. We don't mind if you feel confident enough to do that. We will sit back and do what is expected of us. If not, it's better you stay with us, we will take care of you," I proposed.

Adi continued, *"Look. We have been here before you guys and we understand their psychology better than you. So, it's in our common interest that you follow us, else you guys will have to deal with a disaster."*

Just then, Mr. Anoob Jose, the housemaster of the Chalukya house barged into our dormitory shouting for Arjun and Dhanu. Mr. Anoob Jose was a Keralite. He was fair, tall, handsome, and heavy-bodied. When Arjun and Dhanu went to Mr. Anoob to enquire, he instantly thrashed them up and walked away in anger shouting, *"You irresponsible idiots."*

It took everyone by surprise. I asked everyone to follow me to Anoob's house. Anoob came out and saw twenty students of class 10th waiting at his door. He knew the reason but didn't anticipate such a strong reaction.

I was leading from the front. Adi, Dhanu, and all other senior house boys of class 10th stood by my side. The others who had just joined the Chals in class 10 were standing behind us.

I asked Mr. Anoob, *"Sir, why did you man-handle them?"*

Anoob was annoyed and replied, *"Who are you to question me? I am your housemaster."*

"Being a housemaster, you shouldn't physically handle them, Sir," replied Adi.

"What was the reason, Sir? Please can you tell u.," inquired Dhanu and Arjun.

Anoob explained, *"It is because you guys didn't turn up though I sent a call for you."*

Everybody turned to look at them.

"If they don't turn up, what right have you got to bash them, Sir?" I asked.

"I haven't received any such intimation, Sir," interjected Dhanu. *"Neither did I, Sir,"* chimed in Arjun.

We were furious.

"Whom did you send your call with, Sir?" asked Srikanth. Srikanth was an ex-Moghul who came to Chalukya during our 9th class reshuffling. He looked tough and muscular.

Anoob became defensive. He didn't know what exactly went wrong. *"I sent a word with Shailesh and he told me that he has informed you both."*

"If that is the case, please call Shailesh and enquire with him right now, Sir," we demanded.

Anoob understood that it was actually the mistake of Shailesh and not of Dhanu or Arjun.

"I'll see the end of Shailesh then," he mumbled.

"We are least bothered about that, Sir. What we want is an apology from you for thrashing them without knowing the truth," we demanded. *"You should have at least enquired before taking such an uncalled action."*

Anoob had little choice. He had to render an apology to the defiant group.

It was a great victory for us. Particularly to those who were non-Pandyans. It was also an eye-opener for the Pandyans and particularly their contention that how one so diminutive can take a stand for them. They understood that I stood by my name - RAMBO. They understood that I was reliable. Their fear of being sidelined vanished and they were confident that they would be taken care of.

As time passed by, I went on to become an official cadet of Kumar and Raghuvardhan and an unofficial caddie[13] of Amar and RajaRao.

Cricket brought us together, no matter what the mood. We played cricket in every possible corner of the school. Cricket in the kabaddi court

---

13. Caddie – another name for cadet

was very popular. Kumar was a huge fan of Rahul Dravid and loved playing cricket, all the time, in the kabaddi court. Vamshi (the porcupine) and I from class 10 were his regular partners at the pitch. Kumar, was particular that I had to spend as much time as possible playing cricket with him. Our bonding and understanding were good. I often took liberties with my seniors. Everybody was quite fond of my nature and my way of handling things.

The next biggest event for Grade 10 was fast approaching. The cross-country.

Naik was obsessed with Cross-Country. He had called for a fall-in and announced a practice schedule that was to be followed every day of the year, till the Cross-Country races are over. There were two Cross Countries every year and based on the average performance of both, the winner was declared. As per schedule, the 10th graders were supposed to wake up by 4:00 am and get ready by 4:15 am. Naik was to be woken up at 4:00 am. He joined us depending on his mood.

There were two different cross-country races. One for the juniors and the other for the seniors. Junior cross-country was from class 6th to 9th and the seniors cross-country was from class 10th – 12th. There were separate routes for both. Naik insisted that class 10 students should go for the junior cross-country race and run twenty tracks every day as practice. He also made sure that someone from 9th supervised us to ensure that all follow through.

In the days that followed, class 10 of the Chalukya House, had to be on our toes exclusively for cross-country practice for about one and half hours a day. This was apart from our regular PT and the games period. During practice, we figured out that Manish, a Pandyan who joined Chals in 9th wasn't performing well and also was not enthusiastic about sports. I decided to correct him. Just before the evening practice began, I went up to him and asked him, *"What's your problem?"*

Manish was tall and lean with braces and wore spectacles. He was annoyed at being questioned. He was miffed at Adi, Dhanu, and me for taking decisions unilaterally. But he never had the opportunity to confront us. Now at the first opportunity, he held my shirt collar.

I didn't expect Manish to challenge me; lest hold me by my collar.

"How dare you, bastard!" I began.

"Who do you think you are!" responded Manish.

Even before I could react, Manish was lying flat on the floor. He was gasping for breath. I turned around to look. Dhanu had kicked him straight on his chest. I glanced at his foot. He had worn canvas shoes.

"You bastard, how dare you ask that question," shouted Dhanu.

"Do you understand now, who he is? You fucker, stay within your limits," shouted Adi. All within earshot had gathered there. Manish was still lying on the floor holding his chest in pain. He was whistling and wheezing while trying to breathe. *"Careful Adi! He is is an asthma patient,"* said Pandu.

"Then, he is expected to behave accordingly" retorted Srikanth sternly.

The news spread. Seniors rushed in to find Manish lying flat on the floor. We carried him to his bed. No one said anything. He had clearly crossed his limits. However, we were concerned about his safety. He soon recovered and sat on this bed gingerly.

I looked at Manish and quietly said, *"First learn to breathe properly and then you can think of taking on us. Don't ever think of messing with us again."*

After this incident, everyone knew better than to misbehave. Manish got the strike of his lifetime, but nobody felt sorry for him. He stopped looking for revenge and began practicing with the team.

The day of the cross-country race neared. We had practiced rigorously for two months. On Friday night, post-dinner there was a fall-in at the kabaddi court, for all the class 10 students. We were tense. The class 12th boys arrived for the fall-in.

"I think you have had the maximum practice and I am sure you will not let us down," expressed Naik.

"You guys have only seen the good side of us till now, in case anything goes wrong tomorrow, I am sorry to say that we will have to show you the other side," warned Amar.

"When it comes to the matters of the house, all are equal. No preferential treatment will be given to anybody," hollered RajaRao.

"Your fate will hang on your performance," declared Kumar.

"It's all in your hands now," added Raghuvardhan.

Listening to them, fear gripped our minds.

Post fall-in, we gathered and decided to run for our lives. Everybody promised to do to the best of their abilities. Revanth, Arjun, Dhanu, Srikanth, Ramesh and Sanjeev were excellent runners. Vamshi, Pandu & Jyotish, and I were good and all others including Adi were average runners. Though they promised to do their best, they were not sure of their performance.

The basic problem was they could outdo their own performance but beating the performance of their rival houses wasn't that easy. Others didn't have to practice as the Chals 10th did. They were superior at their game. For B.K. from Gupta 10th, Cross-Country was like a cakewalk. He didn't have to put in any extra effort. He came first without much practice. For the Chals, winning the race was a herculean task.

Around 170 participants were expected in the senior cross-country. Tokens were given in descending order to calculate the average of the houses. The biggest hurdle in the cross-country was to cross the school's main entrance gate. It was about 1 km from the starting point in the ground and it was clearly visible but was so far that the runners gave up mentally even before they began. It was a psychological barrier. Once there, half of the battle was won. The other half began when we returned to the main gate after collecting the Token, about six km away from the starting point.

Whenever one reached the main gate, the audience cheered loudly. The audience were those who either didn't participate in the cross-country for medical reasons or those who had already completed their race. Teachers, housemasters, wardens, and all other sub-staff members sat in the audience.

However, that day despite doing our best, we the Chals, couldn't perform as expected. Though we outdid ourselves, we couldn't outdo our rivals. A fall-in was immediately called post cross-country. Our Token numbers were taken and we were collectively taken to task.

"Come here Rambo and Adi," ordered Amar.

We went. Amar asked us our Token numbers.

"136," I replied.

"102," said Adi.

Amar asked me to slap Adi. I didn't have a choice. I slapped Adi.

Immediately Amar slapped me hard and said, *"This is how you slap. Now slap him."*

All of us stood in a line slapping each other. To outsiders, it must have sounded like fireworks. Our cheeks hurt. Tears rolled down our faces, especially those who joined the house in 10th.

The 12th graders showed no mercy. *"Fuck these bastards. They have no sense of responsibility and spirit. You wouldn't have died had you slogged for the event, but now we are sure you are going to die,"* declared Naik.

"Half kneel down!" he ordered.

Our thighs and palms had to be parallel to the ground. Our backs held straight. Half of our classmates were asked to kneel on the thighs of those who were in the half-kneel position.

Srikanth was kneeling on my thighs. My legs trembled, but I didn't have a choice either.

We squatted and held our ears through our legs and got caned on our backs. The pain from the thin cane vibrated all over our back. 30 mins of fall-in caused us so much misery that we wished we had died in the cross-country. We were not even in a position to stand erect post the fall-in episode. We felt as if we had no life left in us. Our faces were pale.

"From tomorrow onwards, I will be coming along with you fuckers for your mock cross-country runs till the next cross-country and I will see the end of those guys who are going to complete the cross-country after me," bellowed Naik.

"I think you got a sample now, if we don't find any improvement, it will become a daily affair from now on," added Amar.

"You hopeless idiots," shouted RajaRao. *"Now get the hell out of here."*

We reached our beds with great difficulty and just lay down.

Meanwhile, the tales from Gajapati house seemed never-ending. To take a break from the regular chores, Rajesh was relaxing in the house during the period immediately after the assembly. Rajesh, alias Razia was a Guptan in 9th grade who moved to Gajapati house post-reshuffling. He had just managed to sneak into his bed that he saw the principal walking towards the dormitory. Rajesh was shell-shocked. He didn't know what to do. Daku was exactly standing in between both the dormitories and looking inside. Rajesh immediately slid under his bed as he walked right inside.

Daku was standing very close. *"Who is this?"*

Rajesh was quiet.

Daku again called out, *"Who is this?"*

Though his heart was pounding, he kept quiet.

Then, Daku slowly prodded Rajesh's shoe with his and asked *"Who is this?"*

Rajesh, immediately responded, as if he just woke up after fainting.

He quickly got up and gave a surprised squeak looking at the principal. He immediately saluted him and continued his act.

Rajesh asked Daku, *"Where am I and what happened to me?'*

Daku, was not sure what could have gone wrong with Rajesh.

He immediately gave him a blow and barked, "*You idiot you have bunked your classes and are sleeping in the dormitory.*"

Rajesh, instantly replied, "*Is that so, Sir? Then I am going to my classes right away, Sir,*" and he ran away from there.

Post-lunch Dhanu and I would race to the washrooms to avoid the queue. One day as we reached the dormitory post-lunch, we found Srikanth very angry and frustrated. He was shouting at everyone; "*You fuckers don't have any house spirit. You have to learn it from the Moghuls* (he came from the Moghul house)." Nobody knew, what actually happened.

He began running around looking for a rod.

"*Rod? Why do you need it?*" asked Adi.

I asked, "*What did the Moghuls do?*"

A very frustrated Srikanth exploded, "*They would have beaten the shit out of me. That's the spirit, unlike you buggers.*"

Everybody laughed out loud including Srikanth.

Saturdays were the most happening days at school, except for cross-country dates. Usually, on Saturdays, a movie was screened in the auditorium. So, we dined early. One Saturday, Kumar called me and gave me a coke tin and a folded paper.

I was speechless and replied, "*Thank you, Boss. I didn't expect this.*"

Kumar smiled and said, "*Sorry Rambo, it's not for you.*"

"*Then? Whom should I give it to?*"

"*Give this to my cousin Praveen, in person. You will find him in class 9 of the Pallava house. Take utmost care.*"

"*I know him, he was my immediate junior while I was in the Pallava House. I will do it Boss, no worries. But should I do it myself?*"

"*Yes,*" replied Kumar. "*It's very important.*"

We left for dinner. I was on a high that day as a hindi movie, Karan Arjun was being screened. I tried to reach out to Praveen during dinner but unfortunately couldn't. During movie time, I found Praveen exactly two rows ahead of me in the auditorium. I was lost in the movie and I passed on the coke and letter to him and instantly forgot about it. Kumar was waiting for the intermission like crazy.

During the interval, Kumar hugged Praveen and wished him Happy Birthday with a broad smile. Praveen replied *"Thank you, brother."*

Kumar expected a better response from Praveen. He asked Praveen, *"How was it?"*

A surprised Praveen replied, *"What?"*

Kumar was surprised and explained, *"The one which Rambo gave you."*

"Ok, I am sorry," chortled Praveen.

"Never mind, tell me how was the surprise?" asked Kumar again.

"Surprise! What's so special about a coke tin," smiled Praveen.

Kumar was restless, *"Not the coke tin, I am asking you about the letter that came with the coke."*

"Oh! I am sorry, but actually, I thought that it was a paper meant to hold the chilled coke tin. So, I wiped the tin with the paper and threw it off," replied Praveen in contrite.

"Didn't Rambo give it to you?"

"No. It was given to me by one of my classmates. He said it was passed on by class 10th boys, stating that Kumar has asked to deliver it to me."

Praveen asked him, *"What was in that piece of paper brother?"*

Kumar replied, *"It had a sketch and a poem; it was the gift of my love and concern for you. But that bastard Rambo has fucked it all up, in spite of me telling him to give it in person."*

"It's okay brother, I understand your love and concern for me, and thank you for whatever you have done for me."

Kumar was totally devastated. He didn't expect this from me.

I was my usual self, enjoying the movie and poking fun. By 10:30 pm the movie was over. I was on my way to the house by 10:45. As I stepped into the corridor, Revanth told me that Kumar had asked me to report.

Just in another two minutes, five others from classes 9 and 10 told me the same.

"He is very anxiously waiting for you and is asking everyone about you, stated Adi. He looks quite serious; I don't know why."

"I think I know why. Let me see." I mumbled and rushed to Kumar.

I went to Kumar with a casual smile and greeted him, *"Hi, Boss. You have called for me?"* Kumar looked coldly. *"Wait for me in the kabaddi court."*

Chapter 11

Class X

Part II – Rising to the Occasion

I sensed that something was wrong. Very wrong.

It was late. Around 11:00 in the night.

I was in the Kabaddi court.

Kumar came holding a hockey stick, looking furious.

"Did you hand over the coke tin and the letter to Praveen yourself?" He asked coldly.

I paled. *"No, Boss."*

Kumar slapped me hard. *"You bastard, didn't I tell you to hand it over personally?"*

"Yes, Boss. You did."

"Then, why didn't you do it?"

"He was just two rows away from me, Boss."

"So, was that a problem? To walk two steps?"

I had no answer.

Kumar landed another brutal blow. I was angry but was helpless.

"What do you think of yourself? You arshole," he shouted punching me again.

The slaps were now harder and faster.

I had begun staring at Kumar now.

Seeing my fierce stance, Kumar got more irritated and started slapping me rigorously.

I bore all the beating.

"Did you see what was there in the letter I gave you?"

"No, Boss," I replied.

"So didn't Praveen, you know"!

I didn't know this and asked him, *"Why Boss?'*

"Because of your negligence," he shouted and hit my back with the hockey stick this time.

"What have I got to do if he didn't see it, Boss?" I yelled in pain.

"Because he thought it was a tissue paper by the time he received it, you fucklet," screamed Kumar and started hitting around my knee cap with the hockey stick.

Though it was unbearable, I stoically stood there without crying.

By 11:30 pm, I was beaten to pulp.

Finally, Kumar got tired of bashing me and sputtered, *"Now fuck off, you bloody bugger but continue to be in Murga position wherever we fall in for any activity."*

"Okay, Boss. Goodnight."

I walked.

My classmates were waiting for me near my bed.

"They can only assault us physically, but they can't tarnish our spirit. Don't worry I am the same Rambo; my spirit and attitude is unbeaten," I declared before passing out on my bed.

Though outpasses were permitted to class 11 and 12 students on alternative Sundays, there were many instances of seniors bunking.

During one such instance, Manoj (a class 12 Gajapatian) bunked to watch the first show of a Chiranjeevi starrer on the day it was released. It was around 10:15 pm and he hadn't returned. The Duty Master arrived at the Chalukya House. When Gajapati House learned this, they had to arrange for someone to adjust for the roll-call. Just then, Kamal (a 10th grader from Gupta House) entered Gajapati house. He was asked to fill the gap during roll-call.

Just before he could lie down on a bed and cover himself, the Duty Master arrived. Kamal wasn't sure what to do. The Duty Master Mr. Biju Toms (History Teacher for class 10) saw him and asked, *"Kamal, are you not from the Gupta House?"*

Kamal lied, *"No Sir, I am a Gajapatian."*

Mr. Toms took a headcount including Kamal; the Gajapatian strength tallied correctly. He still had his doubts. He thought he would cross-check on reaching Gupta House. He walked briskly out of the Gajapati House.

Kamal faced the daunting task of reaching the Gupta house before the Duty Master did. He jumped across two walls of Gajapati and Gupta Houses and managed to hit his bed and cover himself even before Toms could arrive on his bike. Toms was quite sure about Kamal's house. So, he was sure that he would be able to trace the missing guy. But the Guptan strength too tallied correctly during roll-call. He couldn't believe himself. He softly pulled away blankets of all those who had covered themselves to check their faces. Kamal's heartbeat could be heard by one and all.

As Toms, uncovered him. Kamal pretended to be fast asleep.

Toms shouted. *"Kamal, get up."*

Kamal instantly got up and asked *"Sir, what happened?"*

Toms was taken aback. *"I think I am supposed to ask that question."*

"Just fifteen minutes ago you declared that you are a Gajapatian?"

"Yes, Sir, I did. But I am a Guptan now."

"What do you mean by 'A Guptan now'?" asked Mr. Toms.

Immediately RamMohan and others intervened. *"Sir, maybe he was frightened and told you that, Sir."*

Kamal rambled, *"I was scared when you asked me, Sir and I thought you may punish me if I said that I was a Guptan for being in Gajapati house at this hour. I am sorry, Sir. I am a Guptan."*

Mr. Toms didn't know how to react. He mumbled; *"I have to rush to the Gajapati house to trace out that guy whom you covered."* Mr. Toms rushed to Gajapati House. By the time he reached the house, Manoj was back. Mr. Toms was left high and dry. Though he could make out that something fishy had happened, he couldn't quite understand what.

The class 10 students were once permitted to go on an out-pass. It was an age when we were mesmerized by beauty. Being from a boys' boarding school every girl we saw became our first crush. In such desperate times, a movie by the name Premante Idera was released starring Venkatesh and Preity Zinta. Among dozens of guys who were smitten by Preity's beauty were Kaalia and me. Kaalia was from 10th Moghul House. He was the ex-house captain of the Kakatiya House in the 9th grade. Though he had topped his batch, he was extremely grounded and good-natured.

Though Kaalia and I knew each other since class 6, it was Preity who actually brought us together. We would meet to discuss Preity and admire her beauty. Her dimples left us spellbound. We loved her and couldn't stop talking about her. She was my first crush in cinema and Kaalia's second love after Urmila Matondkar.

One day, Raghuvardhan noticed that the fans and lights weren't turned off. A few taps were left open. It was the responsibility of Class 10 students to ensure that they are all in order. Raghuvardhan was very particular about these things. He called for a fall-in post-lunch. Everybody was scared about the fall-in, except me. After all, Raghuvardhan was my boss and was lenient with me. I promised to handle it myself and asked nobody to report.

Raghuvardhan reached the kabaddi court and was shocked to see no one except me. He was furious and yelled, *"Where are all other fuckers?"*

I politely explained, *"Boss, Adi has gone to dhobi ghat on Amar's call. Dhanu to post-office on RajaRao's call. Revanth to Gupta house on Naik's call. I gave reasons for everybody."*

After hearing patiently Raghu smiled., *"Rambo, I am sure if you had not attended this fall-in, everybody else would have been present."*

"That's true, Boss. But I had to attend to inform you, Boss," I smiled.

"I knew it, you ass." Raghu patted my back.

Unfortunately, as Raghu turned around, he saw the emergency tap leaking. He lost his temper and I had to face his wrath.

It was Monday and everybody was in a special assembly. The results of the dramatics competition were about to be announced. As the winners in different categories were announced, the tension among the participants was gripping. In the process, Rehman, The Hulk a 10th grader, from Moghul House was under a lot of stress. Kaalia was sitting next to him in the auditorium.

He asked *"Rehman, what happened dude? Why are you so anxious?"*

"Can't you see they are about to announce the best actor in supporting role award?"

"I know that. But why are you so worried about it?"

"Because, I was a performer," fretted Rehman.

"I see. What was your role by the way?" asked a shocked Kaalia.

"Don't you remember I was the maid-servant who was shocked to see my Master being killed by a ghost? I had dragged his body from the spot."

Kaalia, couldn't stop laughing. *"If I being your classmate didn't notice or remember that you were a part of the drama, do you think the judges might have even noticed you?"*

Just then the award for best actor in a supporting role was announced to someone else. Rehman was embarrassed and realized how foolish he was. He too laughed with Kaalia.

The second cross-country was fast approaching. We had put our heart and soul into practice. We had no choice, but to perform. The night before the cross-country, the class 10 students of the Chalukya house sat together and decided no matter what tomorrow's 30 mins are going to be the most crucial moments of our life.

"We have to perform; else we will perish. Nobody can save us. This is going to be our last race as sloggers. Let's make it most memorable," said Dhanu.

Everybody was up by 5:00 am. The house buzzed with energy.

"Just do it, guys. Do your best, else you will compel us to give our best," warned Amar smiling.

"No Boss, I think we have already got the best from you, hope not to get it again," replied Adi.

By 6:00 everybody was at the starting point of the cross-country waiting for the clap.

"Don't look at the bloody entry gate," I shouted to my mates.

"Let's run for our lives and for the spirit of our house," shouted everybody.

The shrill whistle signaled the start of the cross-country.

Cross-Country had no fixed strategy. A few guys sprinted a kilometer then walked and then again sprinted. Few ran at the same pace throughout the race, while others like me improved their pace progressively. What finally mattered was the Token number. Among the 170 or so participants, no one was in sync with the other. Everybody was racing ahead in their own style. Few from classes 11 and 12 were comfortably walking and chatting. Except we Chalukyans.

The class 10 guys ran for their lives. The cross-country results totally depended on their performance. In the race, they had to run for 6 km at a stretch and collect a Token at the finishing point and run back to the starting point and collect their final Token. The first Token collected is important because only by producing it at the endpoint will they be receiving their final Token. Few of the Gajapatian and the Moghul class 12th students who walked leisurely compelled the 10th students to hand over that Token to them so that they could return without even going to the first milestone.

Thereafter, they had to run and return within time with a better Token number. But in the case of the Chalukyans, nobody relied on anybody. They all ran for the glory of their house and to uphold the tradition of winning the cross-country trophy. Kaalia had managed to snatch one Token in the previous cross-country. When it was confirmed that the same-coloured Token was given at the endpoint, he simply turned back and completed the race with an unbelievable Token of 160.

The Chalukyans of class 10th, were doing their best.

While returning to the finishing point, a Guptan class 10 guy, Srinivas, ex-Pallavan comfortably overtook RajaRao and Pandu of the Chalukya House. RajaRao was infuriated. Srinivas was hefty but a fast runner. He ran at a steady pace and overtook them finally. RajaRao was annoyed. He ordered Pandu to overtake Srinivas at any cost.

Meanwhile, Revanth, Dhanu, Arjun, Srikanth, Sanjeev, and I finished our race comfortably and were cheering for others from the other side of the finishing line. From where we stood, we saw Srinivas, Pandu, and RajaRao at the entry gate. There was loud cheering heard for Pandu. We cheered loudly for him; it would be devastating if he doesn't surpass Srinivas.

Pandu sprinted as hard as he could but couldn't overtake Srinivas.

RajaRao was right behind Pandu. Pandu shivered at the sight of RajaRao. He saw Raja's face. Angry. Fierce. Cruel.

Our Token numbers were well above 145, but Rao's contention was not the Token. It was the humiliation. Rao asked Pandu to ask everybody to fall in at the house, in another 15 minutes.

"I will see you there." RajaRao's voice was chilling.

Pandu was terrified. He told me, just what happened - during the cross-country.

I told Pandu, *"Take a deep breath and relax. Now that it is done, there is no point in being anxious. You tried your best. Hard luck buddy. Had Srinivas known about this he would have backed off. But then, that wouldn't have been fair. So, let's face it, no matter what."*

"This is certainly not the first time. It will pass." I cajoled him with a smile. It seemed to mollify Pandu, though he knew what was in store for us.

As everybody assembled in the Kabaddi court, RajaRao came with a hockey stick and hit Pandu straight on his knees. Pandu collapsed crying.

"You bastard, you bloody couldn't overtake a balloon-sized Srinivas even after months of practice. Shame on all of you, bloody bastards," he shouted.

The atmosphere was blood-curdling and nobody could utter a word.

"Who all came after Srinivas?" asked Amar.

"Almost 50% of the runners were after him. What a shame?"

"What do we do with you guys?" asked Naik. There was no response.

They divided class 10 guys into two groups i.e., those who came before and after Srinivas. Those who came prior were asked to slap those who came after him. Being slapped by class 12 was better than being slapped by our own friends. We couldn't hit them hard and in turn, had to receive it from our seniors and that cyclic process of slapping continued for a while, till all our cheeks became like cherries.

The atrocities lasted for thirty minutes and immediately after an exhausting cross-country. It took a heavy toll on everybody. But we had no choice. All in all, we had done our best and everyone had improved their Token number by 10 compared to the previous Token numbers, but that wasn't good enough, particularly for RajaRao because neither he nor Pandu could overtake Srinivas. It was more about that.

The board exams for class 10th and 12th were nearing. We slowly started getting into studies. We sat up late in the study hall and had tea to keep up awake, post-dinner. During a lunch break, I met my Boss Mahi (Guptan) and promised him that I would serve him tea that night.

"It's been a long time Rambo. I'll definitely wait for it," replied Mahi.

Around 10:30 pm the tea arrived for the Chalukyans.

I was eagerly waiting for it. I knew that Mahi would be waiting for me. I filled a glass and before anybody could see me, I kept it at my window, walked around the house and collected it from the other side of the window. While I was on my way to the Gupta house, I spotted Raghuvardhan, my Chalukyan Boss with his friend from the Moghul house standing under a lamp at the T-junction connecting the Gupta house to the Moghul house.

Before Raghuvardhan could spot me, I rushed to him saying, *"Hey Boss, you have no idea where all I have searched for you. Here! I brought this for you,"* I handed him the glass of tea.

Raghuvardhan was pleasantly surprised.

"Thrilled!" he declared to his friend, *"Rambo is the best. Do you know anyone serving his Boss as our Rambo does?"*

I was all the while thinking of Mahi at the Gupta house.

"Okay, Boss, I need to move now. Please enjoy your tea." I rushed back to my window. Taking another glass of tea, I took another route to the Gupta house. It was already 11:00 pm. Mahi was restless and was waiting for me.

"Hi Boss, here I am!" I shouted.

"You bastard, you almost killed me. I have been standing here so long," shouted Mahi.

"I know," I narrated what happened a few minutes ago.

Mahi couldn't stop laughing. *"Only you can do it."*

We laughed together.

Chalukya House was the winner of the cross-country that year. It was great news for us. We deserved to win and celebrated with joy. With that, the bonding and mood of the 10th and 12th grades improved considerably. We spent a lot of time playing cricket in the kabaddi court and chatting. One such day Vamshi went to the senior dormitory. Amar asked him to apply oil. As he was doing so, Amar asked him to apply oil on his sidelocks.

Vamshi went to Amar's locker and started looking. *"What's up Vamshi?"* asked Amar

"Boss, I am searching for the side locks on your cupboard."

Amar burst laughing. *"You fucker, these are what side locks mean,"* he pointed to his hair. Vamshi couldn't stop laughing.

The board exams began. Everyone from class 10 and 12 pored into their books. Luckily for us, the syllabus of class 10 wasn't very difficult when compared to class 9. We didn't take it lightly, for we all wanted to score well. Adi was by my side pushing me in mathematics particularly. Arjun was helping Dhanu and likewise, everyone who was in need of guidance was taken care of.

For class 12th guys, it was a tough task. Their syllabus was vast and complex. They formed teams to help each other. The lights were always switched on as students were present in the study hall throughout the night. Everyone did their best in their board exams. Finally, it was time for class 12th students to bid farewell.

Class 12 students hosted a grand party for their housemates. It was a fantastic night. We danced in joy. Dhanu and I took the stage by storm as we all celebrated our journey of togetherness. It was an emotional moment for everyone. For class 12 it was their last night at school. They felt that seven years just passed by like a breeze. They shared their stories of hardship and joy and wished us the best. We would now be moving to class 11.

Class 11, was always considered to be the best period of anyone's life in the school. Though class 8 does give everyone a fair share of freedom, there was no freedom from fear. They always feared someone is above them and they are being watched. But class 11, was another thing altogether. It was like a one-way road with no speed limit. It was completely up to the individual as to how he wanted to live.

On the day of the farewell, the school administration made an announcement. The system of merging boys of grade 9 into the senior houses was repealed. As per the new guidelines, for the following year, all students from class 11th would be in a single house. Similarly, grade 12 would be in another house. Grade 9 and 10 boys would be accommodated into the other two senior houses along with few from grade 8.

The remaining boys of grade 8 would be accommodated along with classes 6 and 7 in the junior houses.

The classes were shuffled because it was known that 11th and 12th graders used their seniority to harass students of class 9th and 10th and nobody was really focusing on studies. Classes 10th and 11th vehemently opposed the new organizational structure. They opined that the spirit of sportsmanship would be diluted and the quality of competition compromised. The house would lose its soul.

All the class 10 and 11 students assembled to protest. The management was even more convinced that they are right. They were now sure that by reshuffling the houses the seniors will lose their hold on the juniors. Monitoring class 11th and 12th students would be now easier.

The 10 and 11th graders wanted the existing structure to continue. We felt that it really kept us competitive and, on our toes, to perform better. We protested, but nobody was interested. The administration felt that we could be easily managed if isolated from the remaining grades, and hence their decision was right.

The class 12 students, who were leaving the school, felt sorry for us. The administration didn't heed our protests. The juniors were elated with the change in the structure of the houses.

For us, it was going to be a new beginning in a completely new setup.

Chapter **12**	**Class XI**
	Part I – Evolution of the EGO

For the first time since I joined the school, I eagerly looked forward to going back post-summer vacations. I am sure all Saikorians look forward to such a day. Without any fear or anxiety. We had come through fires of hell. It was like looking at the earth from the sky. This year we expected freedom from fear and wanted to live our lives to the fullest. In all my dreams I saw myself floating in the air. The vacation seemed never-ending. We couldn't wait to go back to school.

Finally, I boarded the train back to school. This was the second time that I was happy to travel to school. My first happy journey to school was in happy pride, after gaining admission. How I had changed!

I was anticipating a whole new life. The juniors would cater to our whims and we would be their Masters. Our roles would change from the oppressed to the oppressor. We had braved bitter atrocities from the seniors knowing that one day, very soon, we would be the Masters. I felt like I had scaled Mt. Everest. We didn't have to hide anymore. Now it was the turn for others to hide. The thrill of power felt ecstatic.

We reached school and understood that massive changes came into effect. The students promoted to class 11th were shifted into the same house i.e., the Gajapati House, and the class 12th students to the Chalukya House. We didn't have direct access to the juniors. Class 9th and 10th students were assigned to the Gupta and the Moghul houses. They would be captained by the class 12th students. Class 6th, 7th, and 8th students were reshuffled among all the junior houses, to be captained by Class 11th guys.

The setup had changed. The competitive spirit among the class 11th students was transformed into a cooperative spirit now. We have been pitted against each other till now in our inter-house competitions. Now we had to work as a team to compete with class 12th. This new setup was a blessing in disguise for me and my friends from Chalukya house as we were no match against other houses as far as sports were concerned. But we lost a lifetime opportunity to up our game and team spirit.

The main motive of this reshuffle was to flummox the class 11 and 12 students. One, the juniors would be safe. Two, since there was familiarity within 11 and 12, and the administrators thought there would be clash of egos within the grades.

Luckily for me and my batch-mates, the reorganization of houses only added to our strength. The houses were reshuffled when we were in grade 9 but we continued to be together. In class 10, we understood and bonded with each other really well. We also had good connections with our earlier houses. So, nothing had really changed. It was like all the rivers joining into the same sea.

Once we were back at school, the first major decision we had to take was to choose between Biology and Computer Sciences. M.P.C (Mathematics, Physics, and Chemistry) and English were mandatory. There were many rounds of discussions and counseling to decide between the two.

We argued on the merits of the two subjects.

Deepu opined: *"We have studied Biology since the 6th grade. Computers is absolutely a new subject. It's better to trust a known devil than an unknown angel."*

Suri added, *"It would be tedious to draw so many diagrams. Also, we are not good at it."*

"Biology can be learned by studying but Computer subject is about coding. How good are we at coding? I am good at drawing. So, does taking Biology make more sense?" I argued.

Dinu and Dhanu opined, *"Since we have passed our 10th grade with science, it's better if we continue with the same and we can appear for both Engineering and Medical Entrance exams."*

"If we take Computers, we can learn something new. But, is that really required now?" responded Deepu.

Suri added, *"If drawing is pertinent to Biology and I know drawing will I score in Biology? But with Computers I don't even know what I don't know?"*

"I felt I am equally bad at both subjects. So, I will go with the flow," said I.

B.K reasoned, *"We are good at computer games but I am not sure that taking Computer Science as a subject is wise."*

Dinu and Dhanu felt that Computer Science was not a subject even worth discussing.

Most of the toppers in our batch opted for Computers. Among those who opted for Biology about 70-80% of them were from the senior house while in grade 9. They had to battle hard for securing mere passing marks in 9th grade. So finally, a whole group - Suri, Deepu, B.K, Dhanu, Dinu, and I among others, decided to study Biology. Biology formed the A section. The top scorers opted for Computers, which formed the B section of class 11. Life's impacting decisions are sometimes taken on flimsy grounds without relevant research or advice.

Mr. Rao, the senior Master of the School, entered our lives as a faculty. He had addressed us on our first day at school. He hadn't made an impression even then. Tall and athletic, his snow-white hair gave him an astute demeanor. He taught a part of Physics to class 11th and 12th students. The other part was taught by Mr. Ramanujan. Mr. Rao had a separate office for himself as a senior Master. He was disciplined and expected the same from his students. While I believe it is good to be disciplined, expecting it from others is asking for disappointment. *Expectation laid the foundation for conflict.*

Mr. Rao wanted to control the seniors right from the day they joined grade 11. He felt that it's always better to nip indiscipline in the bud. Till we passed grade 10th, Mr. Rao was a stranger to us. Neither of us had to acknowledge each other. But now we would be together for the next two years.

It was our second period and the first physics class of Mr. Rao. We belonged to the A section. He taught us with the help of slides and pictures to teach us. Deepu, Suri, and I sat on the last bench. We understood nothing. We looked at each other's faces and smiled.

The moment the class got over, Deepu and I rushed to the washrooms. Right behind us stood Mr. Rao watching us in astonishment. We didn't give any damn about him watching. He left the washrooms. As we came out of the washroom, we saw Mr. Rao standing right there waiting for his turn.

Mr. Rao called out my name, "*My dear friend Ramakrishna, didn't you notice that these washrooms are meant for STAFF ONLY?*"

Meanwhile, Deepu slowly slipped away from the scene.

I politely replied, "*Sir, we needed to use the washroom and when the pressure is high, we tend to ignore the signboard to relieve ourselves. Sorry for the trouble, Sir,*" and quietly walked away. Mr. Rao then remembered that even his pressure was high and went in to relieve himself.

We felt that Class 11, was worth the five-year wait. Days passed by, in fun and entertainment. Life becomes bliss when we are in the now and that's what exactly happened with us. We were just going with the flow of life. We never knew life can be so light and so spirited if we just live in the moment. Soon the quarterly exams knocked at our doorstep.

All the while we attended class as we were supposed to, but we never attended to understand what is being taught. It hardly mattered to me. I was confident that I would pass. Of course, I was thinking about the annual exams and not quarterly. By now I was used to failing in both quarterly and half-yearly exams and moreover, I knew that my progress report is not going home. So why worry?

I was always scared of mathematics. But now all subjects equally scared me. Science till class 10 was a single paper, had now mutated itself into three - Physics, Chemistry, and Biology. All three were equally threatening. By God's grace, English was manageable and still a compulsory subject. I and friends sleepwalked through the last couple of months and had no clue of what was happening in class, though we attended all lectures.

The E-Week (Exam-Week) finally arrived. It was the time to prove our might. We were the self-proclaimed Gladiators of the E-Week. My friends and I decided to '*live up to our glory*'. So, we did the best we could. I was leading from the front and didn't succumb to the pressure of the question papers. Instead, I counterattacked the questions by offering my own theories and solutions. I took multiple supplementary sheets to prove my point and disprove the textbook. Emboldened by my first surprise attack, I delivered with the same panache in all the subjects. I felt like a blind bull raging in the fields.

A week after the E-Week, the paper correction was in the process. During the second period in the B-section, our chemistry teacher Mr. Shankar was correcting the papers of class 11- A section students. Just before the strike of a bell for the breakfast, he came across an answer sheet which was bulky in size and said aloud, "*I think finally I found someone from A section who has really written something valuable.*" Everybody from the B section was curious to know who it could be. So, during the fall-in before breakfast, the discussion was about what Mr. Shankar just referred to in the class.

Everybody thought that it could be Aswani Kumar the topper of the A section and also one of the toppers of the class. Aswani shook his head – *"No, I haven't taken any supplementary sheets."* Everyone kept guessing. Then they saw me, with a sly smile.

"Is it you by any chance, Rambo?"

I was delighted, *"Yeah, That's me."*

Suri and Deepu were annoyed. *"You bastard, how did you do that?"*

"I don't know how but the answers just flew through my pen as if I was writing a poem." I smiled.

"Can't believe it's really you," snickered my friends. They demanded that I read out my chemistry poems.

"Let the marks speak for themselves. I think I am worthy enough to be taught. By the way, I think you guys might not have known, Chemistry is a subject I understand!!!!!"

"Oh Really!! We didn't know that," the boys laughed disbelievingly.

The corrected answer papers were being distributed. We were in the Chemistry lab when Mr. Shankar began distributing our answer sheets. He called out names in the order of our roll numbers. Deepu was the first among the three musketeers. Mr. Shankar called out his number and as he went to collect the paper.

He yelled at him. *"Disgusting performance!"*

Deepu bowed his head and looked at his paper when he sat down to find 5 marks on his sheet. It was Suri's turn. He thought *if Deepu had scored 5, what would be my fate?*

Mr. Shankar looked at Suresh and hollered, *"Being a house captain, is this your score? Pathetic!"*

Suri returned quietly and looked at his paper to see 3 marks. Most of the class scored below 10 except for a few chosen toppers.

Meanwhile, Suri and Deepu started asking me, *"Is that really your paper? What did you write dude?"*

I smiled. *"I wrote what I know dude, and I told you that Chemistry is in my blood."*

Both Suri and Deepu gave me a sarcastic look. Mr. Shankar called out my roll number. Everybody was waiting to know my score. I walked up to Mr. Shankar with pride and confidence. Mr. Shankar looked down at me and didn't speak a word. He just threw my paper on the floor. *"I don't have any words for you. If you had to score what you scored you shouldn't have wasted so many papers in the first place."*

The entire class broke out into laughter and so did I. Suri and Deepu gasped, *"Thank God we don't have Chemistry in our blood, and by the way how much can we score if Chemistry is in our blood?"*

I replied, *"I think Suri too has Chemistry in his blood. So, he scored just as much as I did, but the only thing is he didn't take as many supplements as me."* We laughed.

With that, I knew what to expect in my other papers. As predicted, I scored half-mark per supplement in mathematics. But one striking similarity in both chemistry and mathematics is that I scored 3 marks in each subject by writing 6 additional supplements and scoring a big ZERO for the main sheet if taken in the literal sense. Paper I and Paper II were for 50 marks each. I wondered that if I had to get passing marks at this rate, I had to write 80 bloody supplements in 3 hours. I could only laugh at this.

Feeling sleepy was nothing new. We were more tired than sleepy. After a particularly exhausting morning, I felt my head droop and my shoulders agreeing to a complementary slump over my desk inside the classroom. Neither the warm air nor the direct sunlight from the window on my face deterred me and I slept without a care. My friends sitting in front of me shifted slightly so that I should not be sighted and were successful, till I began snoring.

Our mathematics faculty Mr. NagaRaju was writing on the board and the boys were busy writing it down. For a change, may be because of the scoldings the class got just a while ago the class was unnaturally quiet. The snoring was loud enough to pass through a quiet classroom to an angry teacher. He yelled, "*You bloody Ramakrishna, how are you even able to sleep, when I'm going sleepless after seeing your marks.*" I woke up and muttered, "*Sir, you are only seeing at my marks but not the amount of energy I spent in writing all those supplementary sheets. I too need rest, Sir.*" He was speechless.

After the results were announced, all the failures were asked to meet Daku - The Principal in his office. We celebrated. It was a proud moment for us. Never did even a topper walk into the principal's cabin with so much confidence and sense of achievement as we did. Our perspective was that even the principal had to push us to perform better. Our achievement mattered not only to ourselves but to the entire administration as well.

As we walked into his office, Daku looked fiercely at us. But for a couple of students, almost all of us had failed in all the subjects except for English. Everybody was pretty cool. It felt comfortable to be in majority. Not one of us actually regretted failing. Daku was perplexed to see us full of confidence and our heads held high. He was shocked to see the house captain Suri, School vice-captain Yagna, and a few more Prefects in the same group as us. He started by asking each of us about our marks and how many subjects we failed. He began with the class Prefects.

"*So, Mr. Suresh, how many subjects have you failed and what were your marks?*"

Right beside Suri stood Deepu and I with our heads bowed, laughing. We bit our lips to avoid any sound.

Suri had no answer.

"*What kind of example are you setting to others as a house captain?*" he thundered

Suri was quiet.

I began pressing his foot. Suri had to bow his head. He didn't want Daku to see him laughing.

"*So, Mr. Yagna, what about you?*"

Yagna muttered; "*I am no different Sir.*"

"*What?*"

"*I am sorry for letting you down Sir. It won't be repeated, Sir.*"

Suri thought *it's better if I don't give any such commitment.*

Daku began ripping us one after another. "*Are these the marks for 100 or 10 he asked?*"

I whispered, "*We haven't verified, Sir.*"

Daku heard that. He looked at me and asked "*What's your name?*"

Even before I could speak, someone from the group whispered "*Rambo, Sir.*"

"*What?*"

I responded, "*Rambo, Sir. Sorry Ramakrishna, Sir.*"

"*So, what's your score?*"

"*100, Sir.*"

"*What?*"

"*Sir, it is 100 in all the subjects put together,*" I replied.

Daku was infuriated. He shouted. '*Are you eating grass or what?*"

Just then his phone rang. We bowed our heads to hide our laughter.

Suri said, "*Don't tell lies dude. Did you really score 100 overall?*"

"*Yes, Man. It was 60 in English and 40 in all others put together,*" I replied.

"*I have to check my total as well then,*" mumbled Suri.

Daku finished his call and looked angrily at the band of mumbling teens in his office.

"*Are you eating grass or what?*" he again yelled at me.

I wondered why he was so fond of grass but kept quiet.

Daku then addressed everyone. "*Aren't you ashamed of your marks? Don't you even realize how painful it would be for your parents to see your scores?*"

Little did he know that none of our parents knew our actual scores since grade 9 and that was the source of our confidence, arrogance, and attitude. Not finding any kind of remorse on our faces, the only option Daku had, was to kick us out of his office.

"Now get the hell out of here. I don't want to see you back in my office after half-yearly exams at least."

We came out of the office as if we had conquered the world. *Now that's all that Daku had to say. if we fail, big deal.*

With that don't give a damn attitude, we had a roller-coaster ride in school. The reshuffling done by the administration allowed us to be at ease and live an unchecked life. Earlier we were divided by our houses and were limited in number but now we were united and we lived '*Unity is Strength*' in every possible way.

Everything in class was shared. We felt comfortable and secure in groups and gave each other equal courage and confidence. The beds in the dormitory were also in proximity of our close buddies. Our juniors were scared to enter our house, as everyone posed an equal threat.

Winter vacations were over, we were back in school. In Grade 11 we were so happy being together that we didn't bother the juniors and didn't dole out the harassment that we faced in our class 9th and 10th. But in case of any deviation from the traditional seniority norms, the juniors had a hard time. There was always a thin demarcation. For those who knew and understood their limits, class 11th students were good. But for those who didn't, it was like a hell. At the end of the day, it was all up to the individual.

As days passed, one day my father visited the school. It was a shocker for me. What could it be? My heart stopped beating. I rushed to him and asked, *"What happened, father? What made you come to school without any prior intimation? Is everything okay?"*

"Everything is fine but you have to come home along with me," demanded father.

"Why? What happened? Is everyone okay at home? What has happened, please tell me, father?" I pleaded.

He smiled. *"Nothing as bad as your imagination. But one of our buffaloes died, Rama."*

"Is that so? When did that happen and what have I got to do with it and why should I come home for that reason?"

"It's because of your crazy habit of drinking raw milk."

"What has the death of the buffalo got to do with my habit in any way?"

"It's because the buffalo has died of being bitten by a mad dog and we are unsure whether you had its raw milk when you just came home during your winter vacation."

"Oh, God! What is the use if I come home now?"

"Your mother is worried and she insists that you should take the injection course as prescribed."

"Do I really need to take that whole course of injections? It's painful."

The half-yearly exams were close. So, if I could manage to go home, for that reason, I don't need to attend the exam. Oh Wow! That would be amazing, I thought.

Somehow, I along with my father convinced my housemaster and the principal and left for home. After giving a patient hearing to the series of events that brought us to the hospital, the doctor advised there was no need for an injection in my case. It was a blessing in disguise for me. *No injections and no exams; wow it was a double bonanza.* Though the injection course wasn't suggested, I stayed back home and went back to the school post-exams.

By the time I returned I heard that Krishna, one of my close buddies was taking weekly out-pass to take injections for dog bite as a precautionary measure. Krishna was tall with fine silky hair and big buck teeth. A group of others including Kaalia were taking homeopathy medicines. I couldn't stop laughing. *"I haven't even taken any injections. Just because I wanted to skip exams, I stayed at my home all these days. Why are you taking all these injections and medications? What's wrong with you guys?"*

It all began when Srinivas fibbed, *"Rabies could have been passed from Rambo to all of us; remember - we shared his snacks."*

Kaalia added, *"Rambo might have shared a biscuit that was chewed by him."*

The conversation became more absurd when Srinivas seconded his comment, *"Yes, I have seen him turning around the bitten side of the biscuit while sharing it. So, it is very likely that his rabies could infect others too. If drinking raw milk could affect Rambo, why won't the bitten biscuit affect us,"* he claimed.

Srinivas was a biology student. He was good at Biology and aspired for MBBS. He thought and spoke like a doctor. So, everyone eventually gave into his line of thought and decided to take medication. On the other hand, Krishna being a localite took the advantage to go home on out-pass using this excuse.

I was flabbergasted by the confidence of the liars and the stupidity of the listeners. Simply made for each other.

"Well then friends, I began, all of you had your share of fun and fear. So let me now share a snack with you by turning around the portion I actually ate," I smiled and we laughed while polishing off the food.

We were in the Chemistry lab for practicals. The half-yearly exam results were just announced the day before. Mr. Rao read out a list of names of boys who had failed again. They were called by the principal for a warning. I was all smiles and thanked the buffalo for having spared me from the list. Then I started poking others as their names were called.

"You are plain duffers. Guys."

"Rambo, why do you call us duffers?"

"Had I really appeared in the exams this time, I'm sure I would have cracked it. I really feel sorry for not being able to appear this time. You, idiots, are so

shameless; despite being fucked royally by Daku last time you still couldn't do any better. I really feel sorry for you and feel ashamed that my friends are such duffers."

"You arshole, you will say so because you didn't appear for the exams this time." complained my friends.

As the names were called, they looked at each other scratching their heads. Just then, Mr. Rao announced my name. I stood up indignantly. *"Why the hell is my name there?"*

I immediately rushed to Mr. Rao. *"Sir, you have been mistaken. I haven't appeared in the half-yearly exams."*

Mr. Rao smiled and replied, *"My dear friend, that's why we have considered your quarterly performance."*

My face fell and the entire class burst into laughter.

I was annoyed. But it was like a new booster to our group.

"Without you, the glory of the Gladiators will be overshadowed, dear friend," Suri told me.

"Hail the spirit of Gladiators," I said. We cheered. *"What has to happen, happens anyway."*

Mr. Rao was always looking out for boys with long hair. It could be because he has very little hair or because his hair was white. Whatever the reason, he simply couldn't stand long hair. Barber Mutyalu standing under a tree near the senior's assembly was a clear indication that someone would surely be Mr. Rao's prey for the day. Keeping long hair was a status symbol. Combing our hair with our fingers gave us a feeling of confidence and superiority.

Suri and I loved our long hair and remained absent from the assembly when we found Mutyalu around. One day, I didn't see any danger lurking. Everything looked normal. Mr. Rao had set a trap to catch hold of me. I attended the assembly. To my surprise, Mr. Rao arrived at the assembly and then sent word to Mutyalu after catching hold of me.

I tried to escape Mr. Rao. He didn't budge. I tried to buy time. Mollify him. I promised I will get a haircut the next day. Nothing worked. After all, it was after a long wait that he got hold of me.

I implored, "*Sir, I will get my hair cut later. I don't like it to be cut now, during the assembly.*"

Mr. Rao replied, "*I think that day hasn't come since the beginning of the academic year so I don't think it will come on its own if I don't interfere.*"

I replied, "*Sir, this is the first time you have caught me and also the first time I am promising you, so why do you take it to the beginning of the academic year?*"

Mr. Rao replied, "*Well though it's for the first time you always knew that this could happen and you have bunked the assembly on quite a number of times. So, I can't accept your promise.*"

I was annoyed. Mutyalu was waiting. His kit and chair too were waiting for me.

"*Don't cut my hair as you like. If I find it cut more than I want to, I'm gonna see you,*" I warned Mutyalu.

At the same time, Mr. Rao warned Mutyalu, "*If you leave anything beyond the regular length, I will see that you are left with no job here.*"

Mutyalu didn't know how to respond. He looked at me pleadingly. Seeing Mutyalu's plight, I yelled at Mr. Rao, "*Sir, please don't use others to get at us.*"

I asked Mutyalu to cut my hair as instructed by Mr. Rao.

Mr. Rao became furious at my comments. "*How dare you say that?*"

By then the assembly got over. Class 11 students surrounded us. My hair was trimmed. I stood up and shook hair off from my body, took my comb from my pocket, and threw it at Rao's face. "*You may keep it as I don't need it anymore.*"

Mr. Rao took two steps towards me, his eyes wide with anger. He realized that he was surrounded by about sixty boys of class 11. He didn't say or do anything.

Daku and Sparrow were approaching the instruction block. Kaalia signed me to cool off. I could be in serious trouble if the principal and the headmaster knew what I did. We quietly walked away from the place. He would be dealt with appropriately later. My friends advised me that it would be nice if I closed this issue now so that Mr. Rao doesn't complicate things for me. I realized, that they made sense. I went to Mr. Rao's office and apologized. *"I am sorry for being so rude and adamant Sir."*

Mr. Rao replied *"My dear friend you are brave to apologize. Even I feel that I should have given you one opportunity for getting your hair cut."*

I smiled. *"I am happy that you feel so Sir. Thank you for your concern."* I walked out to see both the principal and the headmaster approaching Mr. Rao's office.

"Thank God," I thought while walking away.

There were plenty of cold vibes between the teachers and the class 11 students.

One day post-lunch we were relaxing in the house. Suri was spread-eagled all over the bed and lost in the Debonair magazine he was holding. Mr. Rao entered the house with three other teachers. We were surprised to see them and didn't know the reason for their visit. Mr. Rao called out for the house captain. Suri had to immediately shift his gear from heavenly dreams to reality. He slid the Debonair under his mattress and rushed to Mr. Rao.

Suri's disappointment was quite apparent to those who knew what he was doing just before the teachers arrived. But Mr. Rao didn't suspect anything.

"Sir, how can I help you?"

Mr. Rao drawled; *"I want all of you to get into the study hall right away."*

We were uncomfortable. A wide range of reasons crossed our minds. After everyone assembled in the study hall, Mr. Rao stated, *"We have got several complaints from the junior houses that lot of their things have been missing for a couple of days. So, we have come here for a surprise inspection."*

"We are going to check out both the dormitories for the missing items. Each and every cupboard and mattress will be checked." Suri was thunderstruck.

I asked Suri, *"Has he come to check for the missing items, or has he come to take what he needs?"*

"It's not the time for jokes Rambo."

Mr. Rao asked Suri to be with him while the other teachers began their search.

The teachers were also quite enthusiastic to find something so that they could corner us and take us head-on with evidence. It was the best revenge possible because so far, they have only been at the receiving end. They shook every mattress and opened every cupboard. Slowly they inched towards Suri's bed.

Chapter 13

Class XI

Part II – Rise of the EGO

The clanging sound came closer.

It was the tea kettle on the trolley.

The inspection in the dormitory was going on in full swing. The teachers couldn't find anything in the raid, because we did not have anything that was stolen. But we had a concern - *The Debonair magazine*. Something had to be done fast. I took a glass of tea and entered the dormitory where the inspection was going on. Gently walking up to Mr. Rao who now was standing close to Suri's bed, I lovingly gushed, *"Sir, please have this cup of hot tea."*

Mr. Rao was delighted to see me serving him tea. He couldn't contain his amazement and beamed, *"Thank you, my dear friend, Ramakrishna."* As I engaged Mr. Rao in conversation, Suri slowly managed to pull out the magazine and threw it out of the window. After the mission was successfully accomplished, I smiled at Mr. Rao and left the dormitory. The moment I was out, a huge group of friends surrounded me and asked *"How did it go?"* Proudly I bragged, *"The oldie was exhilarated in being served tea by me."*

Seeing the blank expressions on the face of all my friends facing me, I turned around to see Mr. Rao walking back into the dormitory holding his glass of tea. I had never imagined that Mr. Rao was following me curiously? It didn't take a minute to destroy the good impression I had created. Of course, that didn't bother me. What was more important was we accomplished our mission.

Parents of a few students who lived close by visited them and brought snacks when they visited. Though the food was not enough to be shared with the entire class they surely shared it with their close buddies and neighbours. One night when everybody was in the study hall around 7:45 pm, a few shared home-made goodies in the dormitory with a torchlight on.

Observing this, Deepu came to study hall and took Suri, me, and the rest of us to the dormitory. He turned on the light. It took them by surprise and caused great embarrassment. Of course, we shared a hearty laugh and needless to say the food too.

As days passed, we realized that Mr. Rao was taking extra classes for the A section very often. The biology batch wasn't happy with this. We planned for corrective action; else Mr. Rao would take up all our free time. On checking with the B-section, we learned that the boys from the computer class had bombarded him with questions. Since he wasn't comfortable with this, he stopped taking extra classes. We thought *if the B section could do it, why not the A section?*

We discussed our plan with the entire class. We were prepared for the next physics class. Very soon, Mr. Rao at the beginning of the second period, announced that he would be taking the fifth period as well. The signals were given, *Game on, friends!* The plan was to ask doubts on each and every sentence that he uttered.

The moment Mr. Rao started a topic, Aswani asked the first question. Mr. Rao felt that being the topper of the section, his intent and questions are genuine. He clarified Aswani's doubt. Nobody was concerned about what the doubt was or the clarification given. The class began asking queries - one after the other. Mr. Rao switched over to the next concept. *Sir, I have got a doubt* rose Dhanu, then Dinu, then B.K, one after the other. Mr. Rao looked surprised. It seemed as if section A had woken from a slumber today with a flurry of questions.

In spite of being bombarded with questions, Mr. Rao managed to continue with patience. Finally, the Three Musketeers were nudged into action. Mr. Rao began teaching Alpha Decay. Suri asked the first doubt with great conviction. Mr. Rao answered. Then he spoke on Beta Decay, Deepu asked a question. Then it was my turn. I was sure that the next topic would be on Gamma Decay, but to my surprise, there was no such decay.

I turned to Deepu and asked him for a question. Deepu replied "*I am sorry dude. I can't think of any right now.*" I decided to ask a very intellectual question and stood up.

"*Sir, what is the relationship between Alpha and Beta Decay?*"

Mr. Rao lost his patience. He rushed towards me, duster in hand, shaking his head in frustration. Bending down towards me, he pushed his big head very close to mine and shouted, "*My dear friend, I will break your head.*"

The entire class was shocked. There was pin-drop silence and the class looked in horror at Mr. Rao's action. It seemed that he would break my head anytime. Mr. Rao froze. He realized that he had been pranked and was over-reacting. I thought I was showing Mr. Rao my intellectual side. The bell rang for breakfast. The class was visibly relieved and so was Mr. Rao.

As we broke for breakfast, Suri asked, "*Dude how the hell you could even think of such a creative question.*"

"*There is no space for creativity in Mr. Rao's dictionary, dude,*" I replied and we laughed. "*This and many other such incidents would go on and become folk-lore of the school,*" I bragged. However, what everyone forgot was that Mr. Rao would be taking an extra class that day.

Finally, it was the fifth period. We were nervous as to how Mr. Rao was going to take the class and whether we should continue to bombard him with questions we had prepared. We had not even begun discussing him when he walked into the classroom. Everybody was quiet. Mr. Rao too wasn't in any mood to take the class but he definitely wanted to clear my doubt with regard to the relation between Alpha and Beta decay. So, he called me, *"My dear friend Ramakrishna, there is no relation between - Alpha and Beta decay."* Everybody laughed. Mr. Rao asked the class to do Self-Study.

The cross-country began. The cross-country always reminded me of the Chalukya house. But then things had changed. Juniors from class 10 had become lazy and didn't have any motivation to perform and neither there was any fear of the seniors. During cross-country class 10 students were walking comfortably side-by-side with the seniors. I was annoyed. The students were expected to finish their race, within the stipulated 40 mins; there would be an extra cross-country for those who used to come beyond the set time limit.

Boys who scored below 30 were expected to go for a re-run. Surprisingly 50% of them were from class 10. I did a combination of walking, jogging, and running. I had sent a message to class 10 students who got a Token below 50 to assemble near my bed post-lunch. There were a good number of 23 boys from 10th grade with Token numbers below 50. As the message reached the juniors, they were scared. The word fall-in was still a nightmare.

As per tradition, the juniors were expected to be at the spot of fall-in before the seniors arrived. By the time I and my friends finished lunch and walked to our house, all 23 guys from class 10 were present. The headmaster, Mr. Sparrow was quietly observing. He was just waiting for clues and proof so that he could book the culprit at the right time.

I began my interaction, asking the juniors their Token numbers. As they gave their Token numbers one after the other, Goyal (the school adjutant) walked in and warned me quietly., *"Mr. Sparrow is coming, so it's better to let them off. Let them tell my name when Mr. Sparrow asks them who called them in here."*

I whispered, *"I can let them go, Goyal. But they would still tell Mr. Sparrow that I called them."*

I immediately asked them to disperse. As they were running out of the house, Mr. Sparrow caught hold of a few and asked, *"Who called you?"*

They replied, *"Master Ramakrishna, Sir."*

Mr. Sparrow was delighted to get the prey of his choice.

"Well then, ask Ramakrishna to come here," smiled Mr. Sparrow.

The class 10 guys were in a dilemma. They knew that if Mr. Sparrow took me to task, they would be roughened or they could become my targets forever. My class wished that they could have handled it better, but they had confidence in me, so they decided to wait and watch.

I came out of my dormitory leisurely, wearing shorts, and wished Mr. Sparrow. *"Good afternoon, Sir. What brings you here, Sir?"*

"Well, I think, it's you Ramakrishna," replied Mr. Sparrow hastily.

"What did I do, Sir?"

"Now don't act over smart, Ramakrishna," shouted Mr. Sparrow.

Hearing the noise, Mr. Toms, the housemaster came running.

He whispered, *"Ada, Ramakrishna. What did you do da?"*

I stood firm. *"I did nothing, Sir."*

Mr. Sparrow insisted, *"Then why did you call these guys?"*

I smiled. *"I called them to enquire about their performance in the* cross-country.*"*

"Is that so? Who gave you the authority? Well, I am going to show you your place now. Come with me to the principal's office," whirred Mr. Sparrow before walking away.

Toms was worried. He constantly advised me to say sorry and get it over with.

I wasn't willing to say sorry without actually having done anything.

My classmates supported me.

"Let's go to the office," I suggested defiantly. My buddies followed me to Daku's den.

Mr. Sparrow went into the Daku's office and appraised him about what all happened, then called me and Mr. Toms inside.

I smiled at Daku and wished him. Daku responded by wishing back. *"So, Mr. Dog-bite fellow,"* (Daku addressed me after the dog-bite episode) *"What happened?"*

"Sir, actually the spirit of our school is going down by the day Sir."

"What?" asked Daku.

"Look at the class 10 students, Sir. About 50% of those who came after the cut-off time were from class 10. If this is how they perform now, what can we expect from them in their class 11 and 12, Sir?" I asked the principal.

Mr. Sparrow became speechless and Mr. Toms was quiet.

My classmates were waiting outside the office room and were curious and concerned about what was happening inside.

"But Sir, on what basis does he have the authority to harm the class 10 guys?" argued Mr. Sparrow.

Daku asked, *"Is this true Mr. Dog-bite fellow? Were you trying to show your position of superiority as a senior? Who has given you the right to do so? In what way are you empowered to take action against them?"*

I smiled and replied, *"Sir, I haven't harmed them. I just asked them for their Token numbers and encouraged them to perform better for themselves and for the school. I didn't touch anyone of them as I know that I don't have any right to do so."*

Daku nodded his head in agreement. It made sense.

Mr. Sparrow was on the defensive now. *"SS..Sir, he is trying to divert your attention. He didn't harm them because I entered the house in the nick of time. If he didn't have any intention to harm them, why did he call them to the house in the first place?"*

Toms was beginning to get restless. He did not know what to say and watched wordlessly.

"*If I had that intention, I would have definitely done that before you have arrived, Sir. Has anyone reported that I have misbehaved with them or manhandled them? I have already asked them to disperse even before you reached there, Sir. It clearly is an indication of me not having any offense against them.*" I countered with a smile.

"*But I was told that you have only called those whose Token was less than that of yours,*" asked Mr. Sparrow?

"*That's true Sir,*" I replied. "*I obviously didn't have the moral authority to lecture those who performed better than me. My only concern was that if their performance was so poor in class 10 what would be their performance in their class 11 and 12. You are not even willing to accept my view on performance because you feel that I intended to harm them.*"

I had managed to convince Daku.

"*Yes, Mr. Sparrow., Even I believe that these class 10 students have become lazier after their houses have been reshuffled. How can 23 people below 50 be from class 10 alone, Mr. Headmaster?*" asked Daku.

Toms conceded to smile. He thought *Rama was quite right in not apologizing to Mr. Sparrow. Had he done that, he would have been considered to be an oppressor.*

Meanwhile, Mr. Sparrow had to acknowledge that the class 10 guys hadn't performed well in the cross-country and that he would examine their performance. I looked at Sparrow's face with a beatific smile.

I looked at Daku and extolled, "*Thank you for your thorough understanding of the situation, Sir. We are proud to have you as our principal, Sir. You are the best, Sir!*"

Daku almost smiled but realized he was being flattered compulsively. He nodded towards the door. "*Disperse!*"

Mr. Sparrow left the room in vengeance. As I emerged with a smiling face, my friends understood what might have happened inside.

Toms patted me. *"You were unbelievable"* and walked away.

Mr. Sparrow wanted to milk me but got milked instead. That was a night of celebration for the class 11 students. We decided to make an arrangement for watching F-TV.

Though all the houses had TV connections, the channels were limited to Doordarshan. Cable connections were available only for teachers and other staff members. There was a cable wire running between the Gajapati and Gupta housemaster's rooms. It passed right next to our dormitory. We placed the TV on the last beds of the Dormitory. It was now close to the cable wire running outside. We connected it with a small cable wire that we snatched from the cable TV connecting room.

As we were connecting the cable wires in the dormitory around 10:30 pm, the Duty Master Mr. NagaRaju who was the mathematics faculty for class 11, walked into the study hall. To his utter surprise, he saw the TV box empty. He immediately called for Suri-The house captain. He was told that Suresh was not there in the house. He declared, *"TV is not there in the box and Suresh is not there in the house, surely something is fishy."*

Deepu laughed when he overheard the statement, *"Sir there is nothing fishy about it."*

Meanwhile, I rushed to the dormitory and signaled for the cover-up plan. Mr. NagaRaju was still in the study hall. Arabind walked briskly and then opened the back frame of the TV citing that the TV was not working. So he was trying to mend it. By then Suri arrived from the telephone booth. He had received information about the developments in the house. After seeing Suri's arrival and the TV being repaired in the dormitory Mr. NagaRaju left.

I observed, "*They can't even imagine what we are up to and we can't imagine how suspicious they are about us. Let the drama continue; let's get back to our work and watch what we want.*"

Once in Daku's absence, Mr. Sparrow was made acting principal and Mr. Rao - the acting headmaster. There was a Hindi debate for class 8 students scheduled in the auditorium. Normally, for all extra-curricular activities of the junior houses only the junior houses were required to be present. But Mr. Rao personally took it on to him to ensure that all the students of the school attended the debate competition. So, we were also compelled to attend.

On the given day most of the Prefects from our class including Suri, Yagna, Goyal, and Kamal were out of station attending NCC camp at Kanyakumari. Deepu and I didn't attend the debate as we felt that our presence was not needed. The others attended. As the debate progressed, the seniors sitting behind engaged in conversation, least bothered about the ongoing debate.

Mr. Rao was in charge of the show. He warned everybody to stay quiet. But the herd didn't bother to listen. In fact, after he ordered for silence, the noise level actually grew in protest. This made him uncomfortable. It was a matter of his self-respect in front of the audience and his fellow teachers. So, he took it personally and walked to the rear seats in the auditorium, and began monitoring the seniors.

He saw Pandu having a casual chat with his neighbour complety unmindful of the event.

Mr. Rao walked up to Pandu. "*Stand up.*"

"*Now go to the stage and give a speech on the ongoing debate in Hindi.*"

Pandu smiled, "*How can I do that, Sir?*"

Mr. Rao believed that he was the acting headmaster that day and should be taken seriously. However, this was lost on the seniors.

Pandu snapped, *"I am sorry, I can't do it, Sir,"* in an irritated tone.

An annoyed Mr. Rao slapped Pandu in reply. It was not expected. The entire 11th grade walked out of the auditorium, all shouting at Mr. Rao and calling him names. *"Come on. Let's get out of here and see what he can do,"* said Aditya. So did many others in the group.

Mr. Rao tried to stop them. His words fell on deaf ears. Mr. Rao couldn't take it anymore. His blood pressure shot up. He felt as if he was stripped naked, in front of the entire school and his entire prestige has gone for a toss. He couldn't let that happen. He had to take action now.

He rushed out of the auditorium to stop everyone from walking away. He sent a word to the acting principal Mr. Sparrow and also to all other teachers who weren't present in the auditorium. The incident reached Deepu and me at the house. When Deepu and I joined them, the emotion and intensity of the situation had multiplied. The boys were very angry.

The staff members arrived. It had become an issue between class 11 and the faculty. Most of the staff members were present just because they were compelled to. They didn't appreciate such high-octane melodrama. While there were a few others, who were looking for an opportunity to vent their hidden frustration against us; most of the staff were not in favor of what was happening.

The acting principal Mr. Sparrow arrived. The class 11 students held hands and stood firmly. Mr. Rao was quick to appraise him about what just happened. Mr. Sparrow being an ex-Saikorian himself understood the psyche of the students. He was quite sure that the issue would snowball if it wasn't resolved sensibly and fast. Being slapped by Mr. Rao was a humiliation for the entire class. It was no longer a tussle of an individual. The argument before the slap was limited to an individual but after the slap, it became an issue for the entire class.

Neither class 11 nor Mr. Rao was ready to budge. Mr. Rao wanted action against all those who stood by Pandu, yelled at him, and called him names in the auditorium. For the class 11 guys, it was an attack on their pride. We couldn't understand that after being humiliated in the first place, why disciplinary action was being taken against us.

Mr. Sparrow asked Mr. Rao, who were the guys who created the problem, and what action did he want to be taken against them? Mr. Rao began, *"First and foremost is Pandu Kumar. He didn't obey my orders and spoke to me in a rough tone and thereby compelling me to slap him for his rude behavior. In support of him stood fifteen boys who walked out on me, in spite of me shouting at them not to do so."*

We stared at Mr. Rao as he complained to Mr. Sparrow about us. Mr. Pavan and RaviKumar supported Mr. Rao and Sparrow.

"We will see them at the appropriate time," remarked Deepu.

"What punishment do you want to be given to these 15 boys?" asked Mr. Sparrow.

Mr. Rao declared, *"Suspend them for 15 days."*

"We will see how you will suspend us," we shouted.

It was quite evident that the class would go to any extent as they were deeply hurt. But Mr. Rao didn't show any sign of empathy and only looked for revenge.

Mr. Sparrow thought that it would be better if he could keep all of us in a tight spot and curb our movements.

He ordered the class 11 students to get onto the rooftop of the administrative building. After all of us got on to the rooftop, he arrived there holding an air-rifle. It was already 7:00 pm by then. He ordered everyone to sit quietly on the floor and ordered not to speak a word.

No matter what, schoolboys can't stop murmuring and moreover class 11 was in an antagonist mood now; obeying orders was way out of question.

Mr. Sparrow was walking around holding the butt of the rifle. The clock struck 8:00 pm and the siren for dinner rang. We thought that we would be released for dinner. But there was no such sign from Mr. Sparrow.

I sarcastically commented to Kaalia, *"I think we are having bullets for dinner tonight."* We giggled.

"Quiet now. No murmuring," shouted Mr. Sparrow.

Then finally at about 8:30 pm, Deepu suddenly remembered that we had forgotten to de-hoist the school flag, which was generally done daily before the sunset. Deepu and I had taken over this job to skip PT during the morning hours because we had to hoist it during the sunrise. So, taking that as an excuse, Deepu exclaimed *"Sir, we have done a grave mistake by not de-hoisting the flag."* Mr. Sparrow was annoyed further.

He hit Deepu in his stomach with the butt of the gun and dragged him downstairs to Daku's office. The entire class rushed downstairs and shouted, *"If anything goes wrong with him you will be held responsible – Mr. Sparrow and Mr. Rao."*

About ten staff members were there in the corridors trying to pacify the class 11 students but nobody listened. Mr. Toms was almost in tears and did not know what to do.

Deepu was locked up in Daku's office with Mr. Sparrow. We shouted, *"Mind you, don't invite our wrath on yourself,"* from outside.

Emotions were high. The atmosphere was full of chaos and uncertainty.

	Class XI
Chapter **14**	**Part III – Identification with the EGO**

An infuriated Mr. Sparrow held Deepu by his shirt collar to warn him. Deepu was equally adamant.

When the ego awakens, arrogance speaks and anger listens, everything is destroyed. It doesn't matter to whom one is speaking to, at the spur of the moment. It's all about one being right in what he did and holding others responsible for all the associated problems.

From Deepu's point of view, he made no mistake. Mr. Sparrow thought differently. He opined that Deepu poked fun with an intention to humiliate him during an inadvertent moment of crisis. It all depends on which side of the table one is. Both were right from their own perspective.

"Did you think that it was a time to joke?" asked Sparrow.

"Sir, it is my duty to de-hoist the flag and I only reminded you of it. Unfortunately, you misunderstood. I never meant to offend you, Sir."

"Oh! Is that so? If that was the case, you could have requested politely. You sounded arrogant. Was it not to take a sarcastic dig at me?"

Deepu replied, "*Well Sir, I just stated a fact. But I can't do anything about how you perceived it.*"

While Mr. Sparrow's ego was seeking an apology, Deepu's was seeking revenge. Both felt threatened and humiliated.

Mr. Sparrow was annoyed with Deepu's nonchalant manner. Deepu showed scant regard or respect for his position which further infuriated Mr. Sparrow. He pulled Deepu by his collar and warned him not to show attitude. "*What are you up to?*" he asked.

"*People like you are responsible for the rise of Naxals,*" retorted Deepu angrily.

This statement didn't go down well with Mr. Sparrow. He hit Deepu with the butt of his gun. Deepu's painful moaning was overheard by us standing outside Daku's office.

We began sloganeering, "*What happens outside purely depends on what happens inside.*" The teachers tried to calm us, but nobody paid heed. The situation was going fast out of hand. Mr. Sparrow felt helpless. Nothing he did or spoke impacted Deepu. He was not moved or scared. Mr. Sparrow simply had to dismiss him. As Deepu came out, he was welcomed with applause by all of us.

Mr. Sparrow called for a staff meeting. During the discussion, it was apparent that suspension of fifteen students could cause rebellion or retaliation that could be difficult to manage and could damage the school's reputation. Mr. Sparrow canceled the suspension. It was an unanticipated victory for class 11. Our joy knew no bounds.

As the dinner time had passed, Mr. Sparrow arranged dinner for class 11 on the rooftop. "*Oh boy! I never imagined we will have a moon-lit dinner on the rooftop!*" exclaimed Kaalia.

"*Yes indeed, it is fantastic,*" I agreed. "*Thanks to Deepu. This roof-top-moon-lit dinner is dedicated to Deepu,*" I shouted. Dinner that night was indeed memorable and joyful.

The next morning Sun ushered new confidence in us. We were full of energy and enthusiasm. Mr. Rao wasn't a senior master; he was an acting headmaster. Even after the constant unfiltered outpouring of venom against us, we were unmoved. Mr. Sparrow was restless. He paced about his room in anger. Mr. Rao's voice was raging. *"If they are left unpunished, they would become head-strong and will counter every disciplinary action taken. It will turn into a mob power against the school's discipline."*

"We need to put them down, Mr. Sparrow. The sooner, the better," he finished triumphantly.

Mr. Sparrow was smarting from his defeat. He knew that his earlier decision was made in duress to avoid chaos and he had inadvertently appeased the boys.

During the third period, they sent for the 15 boys who were supposed to be suspended. As a tactical move, the class teachers were informed not to let other students out of their classrooms. It was a planned conspiracy. As we gathered for tea during our tea break after the fifth period, we learned that all 15 students were suspended for 15 days and sent home. We were spoiling for a collective mutiny.

Mr. Toms sensed our pulse. He immediately came with a few other teachers who were on close terms with us and convinced us to calm down.

"It's just a matter of 15 days. They will be back. Anyways they have already left. By protesting you will only invite fresh problems, it is better to cool off now," they explained.

Between the third and fifth periods, they managed to send the 15 guys to Vizianagaram by the school bus, thereby cutting off their access with us. Everything was according to plan. Mr. Rao quenched his thirst.

Revenge sat back and enjoyed the show.

"Whatever happened has happened. Let it be so. Moreover, today is not our last day at school," we thought. The incident had planted seeds of mistrust and hurt in our minds. Mr. Sparrow and Mr. Rao were righteously

protecting their self-esteem. Pavan, RaviKumar and a few staff members were happy with the decision. A joyful night over the roof-top was followed by a day that ended in sorrow. Life is just like a see-saw; every ending has a beginning. Just like every beginning has an ending.

The fifteen days that followed seemed never-ending. Finally, everyone was back. We felt sorry for not being able to do enough to prevent their suspension. However, those who were suspended opined that it was good that we didn't do anything as we would have been brutally put down; our strength was reduced by 15. Moreover, Prefects were out-of-station during the time. On the whole, though the experience was bitter, it gave us a better understanding of the thought process of the school authorities.

The classes progressed as per schedule every day. One day Deepu reached chemistry class late by about ten minutes. It was the sixth period (the first class, post our tea break) and everyone was dead bored by then. Mr. Shankar (Gundu), known for his strictness while dealing with seniors was taking the class.

"Why are you late, Deepu?"

Deepu hesitated at the door and then continued to walk into the class.

"Deepu?" yelled Mr. Gundu.

He stopped and glared insolently at Mr. Gundu. Mr. Gundu kept the book on his desk with a thud and walked up to Deepu.

Deepu was downright disrespectful now. He continued to glare back. An enraged Mr. Shankar slapped Deepu, yelling at him. Finally, he was made to kneel beside the writing board. Deepu showed no sign of remorse. He bent his head sullenly and knelt there. The class was silent. Nobody dared to poke.

It was unfortunate that I too was late that day and worse still, Deepu had to walk in just before me and displease Mr. Gundu.

"May I come in Sir?" I asked.

The class fell silent. Suri waved at me trying to say something. I turned my face to Mr. Gundu. He was my ex-housemaster and we usually interacted with ease, but today there was a stiffness about him. I was smiling as usual.

"*Why are you late?*"

The class seemed to stir. There were hurried whispers.

"*I am sorry, Sir.*"

"*Well get in,*" said Mr. Gundu. I took my seat and turned to Suri.

"*Where is Deepu?*"

Suri glanced once towards the board, and in whispers narrated what happened.

One 'Sorry' was all that it took. I thought to myself.

It was NCC time and I was standing in the first file. On that day our NCC instructor was Mr. Pavan. He was a very enthusiastic and upbeat trainer.

"*Daud ke chal,*" he commanded.

Nobody listened.

"*I repeat 'Daud ke chal'.*"

This time there was a slight change in pace.

Mr. Pavan couldn't understand why we weren't following his command. Walking briskly to the first file he commanded again, "*Daud ke chal.*" This time we began walking briskly.

Mr. Pavan found that in the first file, I was reluctant to run. By now Mr. Pavan had lost his cool.

"*Yeah, you fellow Ramakrishna! Come here!*" He shouted.

I stopped walking and looked at Mr. Pavan arrogantly. Then slowly walking towards him, I turned my fingers through my hair and patted it gently.

"*What Sir?*"

By then Mr. Pavan lost his cool and got annoyed. Without speaking a word, he caught hold of my collar and stared into my eyes. I looked back into his eyes and smiled. He was really furious.

Even before Mr. Pavan uttered a single word, he was surrounded by the entire class. He understood the situation and let off my collar. Without a word, I was back at my position in the first file. The atmosphere was tense. Mr. Pavan was speechless. He didn't know how to deal with us. He realized that I derived my sense of pride from the collective ego of my class.

"Not the right time to take them head-on," he decided.

It didn't stop there. We felt that Mr. Pavan had touched a raw nerve. We wanted to get even with Mr. Pavan.

He was the housemaster of Maurya House, which was bang opposite to Gajapati house.

That day, Mr. RaviKumar was the tutor for Maurya House during study hour. The Maurya house was preparing themselves for the house inspection next day. Deepu kept a watch on the Maurya house that night. He planned to attack that night along with Suri and the other key boys of the group. At around 7:45p.m, Deepu, along with Dinu went to Maurya House where the scooters of both Mr. Pavan and RaviKumar were parked, and slowly slit open their seat covers and returned quietly.

As the siren for dinner went off, Mr. RaviKumar who was going to the mess was shocked to find their seat covers slit. He called Mr. Pavan. Mr. Pavan got wild. While he was sure that, it was done by Gajapati 11th graders, he could not prove it. He raged quietly. *"Mr. RaviKumar, I know whose act it is and I will hunt them down at an appropriate time. Don't worry!"*

Deepu and Dinu bragged to Suri and me. *"We watched Mr. Pavan and RaviKumar helplessly walk around their scooters."* Post-dinner we watched as Mr. Pavan prepared for the inspection. Deepu and Suri weren't content with just slitting scooter seats. They wanted more. They wanted to give Mr. Pavan a shock, he would remember for life.

The roll-call for the day was over. The entire school had gone to sleep. In the middle of the night, Deepu and Suri along with a few other guys slowly went to the Maurya House with hockey sticks.

The intention was simple. To make Mr. Pavan regret his actions. They planned to hurt him for as long as they were there in the school. They vandalized Maurya house; carried flower pots to a safe distance and broke them, ransacked the plants in the garden and picked a few display boards on the walls. All this was accomplished in 15-20 minutes. They returned. I learned all this the next morning and was shocked.

"What you guys have done is unbelievable. Just imagine the state of Mr. Pavan!" I laughed.

Just then, we heard Mr. Pavan's loud voice from the Maurya House. We looked at each other and smiled and continued walking to PT as if nothing had happened.

Mr. Pavan immediately rushed to Mr. Rao, the senior Master, and complained. By the time we were back from PT, Daku-the Principal, Sparrow-the Headmaster, and Mr. Rao-the senior master were all present at the Maurya House. All fingers pointed to Gajapati 11th, but there was no evidence. Tracking the culprit with proof was important and urgent.

We decided not to discuss this incident and the perpetrators with anyone in the class. In a way, it was safer as a secret. So, it was a shock to most classmates, as nobody really knew anything. It was impossible to know who broke the flower pots. They began looking for the missing display boards.

Mr. Sparrow expected the display boards to be hidden on the roof-top of the Gajapati house. The entire house was inspected. He then got on the roof-tops of all the houses. He got the ground checked in case the boards were thrown there. All his efforts went in vain. Neither he nor Mr. Pavan was known to give up. But they had to. They accepted that we had indeed outsmarted them.

After this issue settled down, all those who carried out this plan had their last laugh.

It was becoming difficult for us to carry the T.V set to the dormitory daily to connect to the cable. We decided to plug in the connection directly into the study hall where the T.V was placed. This assignment was taken over by our master craftsman, Vineel. He was my best buddy. In the dormitory, his bed was next to mine. We shared countless stories. He made a sketch of the plan; the wire was hidden well and would be visible only at the endpoints.

The plan was executed. However, every night the connecting wires had to be connected after the Duty Master leaves and disconnected before the last man watching television leaves. Now we could watch all that was aired on available channels.

An excursion was planned for 11th grade. Grade 6th to 11th had an excursion every year. Class 12th was left out because of their board exams. Our class would travel to Mumbai, Pune, and NDA (National Defence Academy) Khadakwasla. NDA was the place we wanted to visit. Visiting NDA is a dream of all Saikorians. The trip to NDA would give us a first-hand experience to explore our future aspirations. We would also meet our seniors; ex-students of our school who were then training as cadets at NDA.

It was the land of our dreams. As students, we knew we had the mettle and it was just a matter of time before we would shine. After visiting NDA, our dream to join the Defence forces became stronger. It took us 5 years to visit NDA and realize what many dream of without actually seeing.

After visiting NDA and meeting with our seniors, we resolved to join NDA. We were happy that we were moving closer to our dreams. If selected, we were just a year or two away from joining the Academy. We were excited and clicked as many pictures as we could.

The next day we visited Mumbai. Mumbai was a land of pretty faces. Starved of female company at school, every fair-skinned girl seemed like a beautiful damsel to us.

We were on our way to Gateway of India. Our bus was stuck in traffic. We were glued to our windows looking out for beautiful girls. Those in aisle seats were standing, not to miss any passing beauty. All of a sudden, inside a car next to our bus, I saw a girl. She was wearing shorts and looked hot and sexy. Her curves were visible through her short red t-shirt. The loose black hair partially covered her face. Suddenly she looked at me. I felt an electric shock passing through me. While I stared at her, she looked away and then bent her head to avoid my gaze.

I shouted out. "*Look down, There's a beauty. She is more beautiful than anyone we have seen even on T.V so far.*"

Within seconds everybody jumped towards my window.

"*Wow! She is beautiful!*" exclaimed Suri.

"*Look at her lips, man!*" giggled someone

"*Look at her legs; I can't take my eyes off her,*" cried Dhanu.

"*She is a bombshell.*"

For some time, it seemed as if the bus would tilt dangerously with all the weight on one side. Just then, while running her fingers through her hair, she again glanced towards our bus. She was shocked to see about 50-60 boys staring at her. She didn't know what to do. Immediately covering her thighs with her hands, she bent her head to avoid stares.

"*No!!!*" cried out everyone as the signal turned green and the bus started moving.

We were back at school. Life returned to normal. Annual exams were fast approaching. We had a fair share of fun all through the year and it was now the time to either perform or perish. Studying was a team effort. Almost all the toppers took charge of one or two gladiators. It seemed that the only way for the toppers to show their merit was by ensuring that the gladiators under their care passed. It was only now that the toppers understood how hard it was for a gladiator to pass an exam.

Kaalia took me on board. Deepu was on his own. Suri was taken care of by Aswani. Our preparation was in full swing. Even the teachers who came as tutors encouraged us. Nobody wanted anybody to fail. When it came to the final exams it was a matter of pride to everyone. On such a day a junior came looking out for Arabind. It was around 3:30 pm and everybody was studying in the recreation room and study hall.

The junior smiled and asked, *"Master, do you know where Master Arabind is?"*

"No, I don't," I replied. *"Did you check for Arabind in the study hall?"*

"No."

"Then why don't you look for him there?" I advised.

The junior returned. *"No, Master, he isn't there."*

"Okay, did you check for him in the dormitory?" I asked.

"No, Master," he replied.

"Check over there too."

The junior returned with a smile. *"No, Master."*

"Have you seen who is sitting opposite to me in here?" I asked.

"No, Master."

"Well then, why don't you take a look?" I directed.

The junior turned around to find Arabind and as he turned back to look at me. I slapped him hard.

"Do you think its fun to play around in the senior house? Even without looking for him in here, how dare you ask me regarding his whereabouts? Don't take our friendly nature for granted. Out now," I shouted in irritation.

He was in tears as he went to Arabind.

Historically very few have failed class 11th. Almost all passed and moreover it wasn't a Board exam. Yet we put in our heart and soul to study and pass. We didn't want to take the tiniest of risks. We had closely watched our seniors when we lived in the senior houses during grade 9. We felt that if we could pass grade 9, we could surely clear grade 11. We decided to hold the bull by its horns - with courage and confidence.

As a few days passed we understood why our seniors attended coaching classes in Chennai post class 11. We knew we would pass class 11 even without knowing what the syllabus was because these weren't Board Exams and with some help from our friends we would sail through. However, we knew that without knowing the basics for class 12 we won't be able to clear Board exams next year. So, we decided to attend coaching classes during vacations.

The final exams were over. The summer vacations began. We left for home as per our train schedule. Those who lived in nearby localities went home by themselves. Suri and Dhanu being localities left on the very same day. Deepu, Dinu, Kamal, Yagna too left on the same evening as their train was scheduled at 9:00 pm that night. Kaalia, B.K. and I waited for the next day.

We decided to go to Vizianagaram, have biryani for dinner, and watch the second show of the night. *Sakhi* starring Madhavan and Shalini which was later remade in Hindi as Sathiya. For fun, we decided to walk back to school (about 12 km) from Vizianagaram after watching the movie. As planned, we bunked and left for Vizianagaram, had amazing Biryani, and then enjoyed the second show. We decided to walk back to school from the movie theatre.

The distance was almost the same as the cross-country race. As long as we walked inside the town it was pleasant. The road had street lights and we were discussing the movie from its making to the star performances and the picturization of the songs. It was a love story of a young couple. So, we were lost in our world of imagination, as we walked across the town briskly.

It was about 12:30 at night. We were out of town now. There were no street lights. Dogs barked. Slowly fear gripped us. We remembered the dog-bite story and the drama that ensued. *"What if a dog bites us now? Last time we were lucky, but this time we may not be,"* feared Kaalia.

The blowing winds created a mysterious hum in the quiet night.

"I think since we wanted an adventure, we are getting one," I commented drily.

We walked briskly. We wanted to reach the school as soon as possible. All of a sudden from nowhere we heard a voice from behind asking us to stop.

"Oh My God! Who is that?" exclaimed B.K.

We looked behind to see a group of people walking behind us at a brisk pace. Who could they be? Why are they asking us to stop? We thought to ourselves and began jogging. Even those who were walking behind us started jogging. They started shouting at the top of their voice, *"STOP, STOP, STOP."*

We thought of running now. I thought, *if we run B.K will go with the wind, followed by Kaalia and I will be the last.* So, we all decided to run together at my pace. We knew that dogs roam at night in search of food.

"Who are these men following us?" we wondered.

We tried to hitch a ride from a passing truck. The driver refused. It was around 12:45 am. No truck even passed us now. The gap between the chasers and us narrowed and we could hear them shouting clearly now. We decided to run as fast as we could, fearing that they could be Naxalites.

Just then a truck driver stopped and gave us a lift. By 12:55 am the truck dropped us at our school entry gate. We thanked him profusely for his help and paid him whatever we had with us before sprinting to our house.

After an adventure of a lifetime and escaping suspected Naxalites, we fell prey to our housemaster Mr. Toms who was still waiting for us knowing that we have bunked.

He started giving us an M.L. (Moral Lecture)

It was 1:10 am.

Chapter 15

Class XII

Part I – Playing Pranks

Six years of school had passed like a breeze. It was the last summer vacation of our school life. The time was crucial as we were expected to be prepared for the 12th Board exams. As planned, we met in Chennai in 15 days.

The majority of us were from biology section. We were about twenty including Suri, Deepu, Yagna, B.K, Dhanu, Dinu, Kamal, Sudha, Pradeep, Verma, and me. Kamal's father was serving the army and was posted at Chennai. He helped us by getting us accommodation at T-Nagar.

We stayed at a stand-alone building on the third floor. The flat had a big hall which was converted into two rooms. There was a mess on the ground floor. The place was about 10kms away from our coaching center and we commuted by bus daily.

The coaching classes were for Mathematics, Physics and Chemistry. All three subjects were a nightmare to most of us. We hardly knew anything. How we managed to pass class 11th was a mystery. We knew no concepts. We decided to pay attention and study diligently at the coaching center.

We attended the first class. We couldn't understand a thing.

"We don't even know the basics dude!" lamented, Suri.

"I think by the time we learn the basics our Board exams will be over," I replied.

We laughed but winced inside.

It was a crash course designed to cover the entire syllabus in 40 days. Suri and I felt that we should have taken this course after studying for the year and just before the Board exams as a revision.

It was futile to try and understand anything. Just relax and have fun. We looked around to find someone beautiful in the class. Finally, we zeroed on two girls. One was a fair-looking North Indian girl. Her personality wasn't appealing. The other one wasn't fair but was beautiful.

As usual Suri, Deepu, and I sat on the last bench and were having fun. Of the 20 boys from our school, about 5-7 were smart. They could solve any problem put on the Board within minutes. In order to get the attention of the class, I would look into their books for answers and shout out the answer. Within days, the entire class started looking at me, whenever a question was put on the black board.

I was overwhelmed by the response.

"I am not able to handle so much attention; it's better you both begin answering now and then." I told the others. Now the class was under the impression that we are smart at studies.

One day, as I answered a question the moment it was put on the board, the Physics master got suspicious and he walked up to me and asked me to solve it on the board. I was in a fix and replied *"The answer is in my mind, Sir, to put it on Board let me first put it on paper."*

Sir said, *"Okay."*

Immediately I asked Pradeep to give me the solved answer. The entire transaction was closely observed by the dusky beauty. Then I went up to the board with beaming confidence. The class applauded.

Our focus was the dusky girl. We began having fun by praising her in our language (Telugu). To our surprise, we found that she started staring at us, as and when she overheard our comments. Very soon we realized that she spoke the same language. By then the damage was done. We wasted our time in fun and forgot the seriousness of our purpose of coming to Chennai.

After having spent most of our vacation time in Chennai, we were back at School. This was our last year in the school. When we saw class 6 boys, we were amazed to see how far we had come. We wore full trousers instead of shorts and were respected and feared among the juniors. Even teachers kept away.

Those days Salman Khan had a lineup of rom-com movies with David Dhawan. Though I was a crazy fan, I thought action suited him better. Gaurav Kunal my batchmate who had joined us in grade 9 thought so too. Anyone who was a fan of Salman Khan automatically was my friend. We decided to write a script for Salman. Salman is a star who had the look and physique for action and adventure films.

From that day, we spent at least an hour every day conceptualizing the idea. We kept ideating and discussing till we decided on making an action-adventure film with a patriotic theme. The idea sounded interesting. We felt that it would be a game-changer not only in the filmography of Salman Khan, but Bollywood as a whole.

We were quite often advised by friends, *"What's the point?"* But we were reluctant to stop there. We would reply, *"It doesn't matter whether Salman signs our film, but we will feel satisfied that at least we have tried to do our best as his die-hard fans."*

While I was busy with this, one day a boy from class 9 entered my dormitory. He was stopped by Krishna. His bed was the first one in the dormitory.

"What brings you here?" Krishna asked.

"Master, there was a call to our house asking one from our class 9th to attend to Master Ramakrishna."

Krishna was surprised. *"Ramakrishna? You are mistaken; there is no Ramakrishna, in our class. Check class 11th."*

"No Master. It is Rambo."

"Oh. Yeah! We have totally forgotten his name. That's cool then. When you go to Rambo, the first question he will ask you is, who is your favorite star?"

"It's Shahrukh Khan Master."

"Thank God you didn't say that directly to Rambo," smiled Krishna.

"Why Master?"

"Rambo hates Shahrukh."

"Well then, my answer would be Salman Khan."

"Right!" smiled Krishna before sending him over.

As he approached my bed, he saw two posters of Salman Khan. One was a solo photo of a bare-chested Salman Khan holding a rope and the other was a picture of Salman and Aishwarya from the movie, Hum Dil De Chuke Sanam.

I saw him standing closeby. *"Who are you?"*

"Master, I am Sandeep from class 9."

"Fine. Who is your favorite star?"

"Who else, Master! It's Salman."

I immediately declared him my cadet and introduced him to my group. Sandeep was totally taken by surprise. All it took to become my caddy for him was a declaration of being a Salman fan.

"Thank you, Boss." He gushed while leaving the dormitory. He thanked Krishna for his advice.

One night, when Mr. Reddy was the duty master, he visited Gajapati House for a routine roll-call. It was around 11:00 pm.

"Why don't we poke Mr. Reddy and have some fun?" asked Dinu.

Dinu and I decided to go in hiding so that Mr. Reddy will be under the impression that two guys have bunked and then we shall start making a mockery out of it. It was fun time.

Mr. Reddy took the roll-call in the study hall and the other dormitory. As he entered our dormitory, the lights went off. He felt nervous and began perspiring. Panicking, he rushed out of the dormitory.

Once outside, he saw light in the study hall and the other dormitory. Mr. Reddy then mustered courage and slowly returned to our dormitory. With the help of a torch, he looked at the main switchboard and found that the main switch was turned off. He suspected that class 12 boys have planned to bash him by covering him with a blanket. He glanced at the floor and saw two pairs of eyes looking back at him.

Mr. Reddy's suspicion was now confirmed. He shouted, *"Come here you buggers."* He was trembling while shouting. After a very noisy fifteen minutes, Dinu and I who were hiding under the bed quietly rolled out.

"How dare you guys? You are planning to surround and bash me up by turning off the lights?"

Dinu and I were stunned.

"Why the hell would we do that, Sir?" we exclaimed.

Mr. Reddy didn't heed. He rushed out of the house shouting; *"I will see both of you."* The entire house was shocked.

The question was, *"Who turned off the main switch?"*

"Me," said Srinivas.

"Why the hell did you turn off the main switch dude? You should have turned off just the lights," cried Suri.

"Now he feels that we planned to dump a blanket over him and bash him up," exclaimed Deepu.

I smiled; *"He probably has memories of such times."* We burst laughing.

"We should have given him another sweet memory," said Dinu wryly.

The next morning, as we assembled outside the mess for breakfast, a few boys from class 11 asked me, *"Boss, we heard that you guys planned to blanket Mr. Reddy last night."*

I was surprised.

"*Who told you?*" I asked.

"*It is trending in today's gossip,*" they revealed.

As the breakfast began, we found the staff members staring at us.

"*I think Mr. Reddy badly needed it,*" I muttered.

"*It must be quite a while since he got it. I agree. He very much deserved it,*" echoed Kamal - the cultural captain who was very affectionate and humorous.

"*He has gone nuts,*" said Yagna- the school captain.

"*Why is he shaming himself?*" B.K. asked.

"*Crazy ass,*" said Suri and everyone laughed.

Mr. Reddy who was already irritated felt infuriated when he saw us smiling. As the third period began, there was a call from Mr. Rao's office for us.

"Let's go, bro," I suggested. We left for Mr. Rao's office. On entering, Mr. Rao welcomed me saying, "*My dear friend Ramakrishna, what were you planning to do to Mr. Reddy yesterday night?*"

I smiled, "*Definitely not what Mr. Reddy thought Sir.*"

Dinu laughed.

Mr. Rao was shocked and asked, "*What do you mean by that?*"

"*I really don't know why Mr. Reddy, is complaining, Sir,*" I began.

Mr. Reddy who was sitting there shouted. "*Had you been in my position you would have understood it better.*"

"*I didn't understand what you mean by that Sir?*" I objected.

Just then, Mr. Sparrow entered the room.

"*Oh! God. Mr. Reddy has gone crazy. Is there anyone who doesn't know?*" whispered Dinu.

Mr. Sparrow had a crooked smile. "*So here you guys are! What were you up to?*"

Dinu was coolly arranging his hair.

Mr. Sparrow was annoyed. *"Put your hand down Dineshwar. What do you think of yourself?"* He growled.

Mr. Reddy sputtered, *"Sir I was lucky enough to escape their plan yesterday, otherwise, only God knows what would they have done to me?"*

I felt exasperated now, *"Sir, I think you know better than God, Sir."*

Mr. Rao shouted, *"My dear friend, you can't say that."*

I said, *"He has a wild imagination, Sir."*

"Why would we harm him? He had been our physical trainer since class 6," pleaded Dinu.

"I don't know why he is suspecting us, Sir. We never even dream of harming our teachers. Have we ever harmed anyone in the past? No! We don't have any reason, nor any history of bad behavior with teachers."

"Then why the hell were you hiding under the bed?" asked Mr. Reddy angrily.

Dinu began setting his hair again. This time Mr. Sparrow shouted, *"I'll break your hand, Dineshwar. It is better if you stand straight."*

Dinu stood there. Feet apart, casually leaning sideways with a cocky attitude. He looked haughty. I knew I had to somehow cool the situation.

"If we really intended any harm, we would have done so without hiding under the bed, Sir. What was the point in hiding if we wanted to harm you by turning off the lights?" I argued.

Mr. Rao's face relaxed a little.

Mr. Sparrow realized that, if we had planned a blanket attack, there wasn't any need to hide.

"Sir, we were playing hide-and-seek with our friends. We didn't expect you to come in." I explained politely. I hoped they would believe us and let us go.

"We are sorry for the confusion, Sir. But there were no ulterior motives or sinister plan." I reiterated. Dinu didn't bother to even try and explain.

Mr. Reddy looked at Dinu. He realized how stupid he was to reveal this to everyone and make a fool out of himself. After listening to my defense, both Mr. Rao and Sparrow were convinced.

Finally, we walked out of Mr. Rao's office. After this incident, we were looked upon with admiration by class 11th students for our boldness to plan a blanket attack on Mr. Reddy and then turn the tables when we were questioned.

There was hardly anything we could understand. Theories and concepts of Mathematics, Biology, Physics, and Chemistry just flew over our heads.

"What the hell, except for knowing which subject it is, I am not able to make out anything that is going on," I declared.

"I don't see any of us passing the Board exams," moaned Suri.

"I don't understand why our 12th board is so tough when compared to the 10th?" Dhanu complained.

It got only worse. The quarterly exams were no better. We fared badly. We were marched to Daku's den. We got another severe dose of verbal lashings. This time even we were genuinely worried about our performance. There had to be a solution. We had to find it. For now, we could only mutely listen to Daku.

We recovered from Daku's castigation very slowly. Some of us had even started studying. There was a special assembly in the auditorium. The master of Ceremony was a senior teacher, Mr. ShivaRam. The topic of his speech was *'we can take a horse to the water but can't make it drink'*. The topic was relevant to us; we had been in a celebratory mood all these years and had nothing to do with studies. All present were smiling at each other while listening to the lecture.

After that, Mr. Daku called out for one student from class 12 to speak extempore on the Prime Minister Sri. Vajpayee's visit to the USA. Kaalia took the initiative and started walking towards the dais. Now that Kaalia took the initiative, I stood up and gave an expression and pose of having missed out an opportunity to give an extempore speech, and then, after getting sufficient attention and after striking another pose to amuse everyone - I sat down.

But that celebration of joy caught the eye of the hawk named Daku. Daku immediately called me out. *"Mr. Ramakrishna, I feel you wanted to speak on the topic. I don't want you to lose your opportunity. Mr. Nageswara Rao (Kaalia) please let him speak."*

I was in a fix. I murmured, *"Daku - you jack ass."* I quickly took a few pointers from Pradeep and Goyal before walking to the dais.

The auditorium went crazy. I began my speech, with *"Respected Principal Sir, Headmaster Sir, Registrar Sir, staff members, and my dear friends - very good morning to all. We know that our beloved Prime Minister has made an official visit to the USA recently. Mr. Vajpayee is a far-sighted politician who has loads of experience and vision for the nation, just like our Principal Sir has for our School."*

Sri Vajpayee made this reciprocal visit to the USA in Sept 2000 after the US President Mr. Bill Clinton visited India in March 2000. It was after over 20 years that a President of the USA had last visited us - President Jimmy Carter's visit was in 1978. President Clinton's visit is significant towards a revival of India-US diplomatic relations which got strained after India's nuclear tests in 1998.

With this visit, Sri Vajpayee laid the foundation for strengthening relations between both nations based on shared democratic values and proposed a more collaborative approach in trade and commerce. He has underscored the economic achievements of India's post 1991 reforms and the technological advancements being carried out by India. He has proposed to open up more economic avenues between the two countries for further growth and progress of both nations. He also exposed Pakistan, to its dirty politics in the state of Jammu and Kashmir and the state-sponsored terrorism.

Dear friends, the best personal attribute of Mr. Vajpayee is that he too was a Gladiator. After founding the Bhartiya Jana Sangh in 1951 he has toiled for over 45 years, before being elected as Prime Minister of India in 1996. He is a great source of inspiration to all of us. His success story reminds me of the quote, 'Success is never-ending and Failures are never final'. So, my dear friends, Let's take him as our inspiration and not remain stuck with our very own quote saying, Failures are the stepping stones for success. Though we have been failing so frequently we haven't been still able to find success.

Finally, I would like to thank our beloved principal for giving us this opportunity to deliver extempore speeches. It only enhances our confidence and contributes towards overall grooming to be effective leaders. So please understand that whatever our principal does is for our good." The entire auditorium thundered with applause. Everyone started clapping and whistling. Daku was pleasantly surprised. Mr. Sparrow knew that I was taking a snipe at them but didn't show it.

Once again, I appealed to all my friends, *"Grab all opportunities given. Don't wait until you get your turn. Just grab it."* I concluded by saying, *"Thank you one and all."* The entire auditorium kept on clapping, yelling and shouting, *"Rambo-Rambo,"* till I reached my chair. Kaalia congratulated and thanked me saying, *"You have saved my face today."*

"I have! How?"

"I actually didn't even know that Vajpayee visited the USA. I was thinking, the topic was - What if Vajpayee visits the US."

"Every dog has its day," I laughed.

As we walked out of the auditorium, Mr. Sparrow asked me, *"what was the topic given for extempore? Was it P.M.'s visit to the USA or advantages of extempore speeches?"*

I smiled; *"I spoke on the first Sir but I believe you focused more on the second."*

Mr. Sparrow laughed. *"Ok. There is always a next time, will see you then."*

"Sure Sir, thank you'.

Weekends are the most happening days at school. We looked forward to Saturdays. Saturdays were special. Movie screenings. Lemonade. One such Saturday, while we were about to leave for the games, the kettle arrived. Everybody rushed to their dormitories to get their glass tumblers. I rushed straight to the kettle which was on an elevated stand, knelt down to have the lemonade straight in my mouth. Just then, Suri shouted, *"You bastard, don't have it; it is tea. Not lemonade."*

I was fortunate to be safe. Suri saved me. Else it would have been my last day of the speech.

"Thank God!!!" I murmured.

Suri shrugged, *"Thank me, dude."*

"Of course." I felt grateful. Today being a Saturday I expected lemonade. We got tea. In my stupidity, I would have burnt my throat. I should have checked.

That day Gladiator was screened in our auditorium. Everyone went crazy. We mouthed the dialogues even before they were delivered by actors. Everybody was in their Gladiator avatar. Few of them even lost their voice by shouting the dialogues. I felt lucky that I didn't burn my throat.

It was around 10:30 pm. We returned to the house on a high note after watching the movie. By then, the movie Baazigar was aired on DD National so everyone was glued to the T.V. By 11:55 pm Kamal slowly went to the dormitory citing that he was feeling sleepy. Nobody looked at the time. But as the time struck 12:00 am we remembered; it was Kamal's Birthday. Deepu understood why Kamal felt sleepy.

Usually, birthday boys were woken from their beds with birthday bumps and gifts. That night Kamal went to bed expecting the same. But we had other plans. We went to his bed and started speaking in whispers.

"I don't think it's a good idea to wake Kamal now," whispered Deepu.

"You are right dude, he has just gone to sleep after watching two films, back-to-back," agreed Yagna.

"Yeah, he must be tired, let's not disturb him now."

Kamal was getting restless listening to our talk. He was sliding on his bed, with his eyes closed and ears open. Slowly, we threw a bed sheet on Kamal and jumped over him shouting – *"You bastard!! You have acted enough now, wake up,"* and kicked his butt shouting, *"Happy Birthday Buddy."*

Kamal opened his eyes and laughed and we had a roaring party that night.

It was NCC camp time at school. During camps, NCC cadets from other schools joined us. They were accommodated inside recreation rooms. These camps usually lasted for a week. During such a camp a NCC cadet from another school lost Rs. 100. When an 8th grader learned of this, he collected Rs. 100/- from his classmates and gave him so that their house won't be blamed or shamed for the loss.

The missing money became a topic of discussion. More so, an 8th grader took the intiative and collected the amount to save the reputation of the house. I heard of this and called for him. Master Brijesh was a short, cute and cheerful boy. I liked his commitment and solidarity. I declared that he is my cadet. By the middle of the academic year, I had 5 cadets one each from class 6th to 10th. Ramesh from class 10, Sandeep from class 9, Brijesh from class 8, Ratna Kiran from class 7 and Jayanth from class 6. Of course, all of them were either a fan of Salman Khan or pretended to be one.

Not all the movies screened on Saturday were up to our taste. One such movie was Speed Dancer, a Telugu movie with Raghava Lawrence and Monica Bedi in lead roles. Kaalia and I decided to give it a miss and watch OkeOkkadu instead. OkeOkkadu starred Arjun and Manisha Koirala, and was later remade in Hindi as Nayak. The theatre was in Kumaram, a village about 5 km away from our school. Now that we decided to bunk and watch the movie, we planned to have dinner there, where we could eat food of our choice.

Krishna and three others joined us. It was around 6:30 pm. We sneaked out of the gate and reached the main road. *OkeOkkadu* was a blockbuster movie. We were going to watch it for the second time at Kumaram.

We were about 2 km away from Kumaram when we saw a light projecting before us. It came from a car behind us. Very few cars passed these roads. It was 7:00 pm. The car was right behind us now. By the time we realized whose car it was, it slowed down and stopped right in front of us.

Chapter **16**	# Class XII # Part II – Reality Check

"*Mr. Sparrow!*" whispered Kaalia.

"*Well, let it be anyone, now we don't have a choice,*" I griped.

Mr. Sparrow stepped out of his car with a crooked smile. We smiled back.

"*So, Mr. Ramakrishna, where are you going?*"

"*Well, Sir, we are going to Kumaram,*" I replied.

"*But why?*" asked Mr. Sparrow.

"*To watch a movie, Sir.*"

"*Movie? But there is a movie screened today in the auditorium,*" chided Mr. Sparrow.

"*Yes, Sir, but it is not to our taste,*" I explained.

"*Well then, what's your taste?*" he asked.

"*We are going to watch OkeOkkadu in Kumaram, Sir,*" I replied.

Mr. Sparrow didn't know what to say.

Sparrow thought that since he caught us red-handed, he expected us to lie, and then he could take us for a ride.

I prefer to be upfront. We were caught and there was no point in trying to make up stories. A Gladiator certainly can't hide his face.

"*So, Mr. Nageswara Rao (Kaalia), What's up with you? It's quite understandable with Ramakrishna, but why you?*"

Kaalia smiled. "*I too love to watch good movies and have good food.*"

Mr. Sparrow didn't expect such a reply. "*Didn't you boys have dinner at school?*"

"*Not today, Sir,*" revealed Kaalia.

"*We planned that since we are going to Kumaram, we will have some hot and spicy chicken for dinner, Sir,*" I expressed.

Mr. Sparrow was momentarily speechless and then stated, "*Now that you are caught you can't proceed with your plan.*"

Everyone fell silent. I reasoned, "*Sir, even if we go back to school now, it is past dinner-time. If we have your permission, we can go enjoy our night without fear. If you want to take us to task, you can do it tomorrow. Moreover, we are six and we won't fit inside your car, Sir. So please spare us today.*"

Mr. Sparrow agreed. "*Alright, you can proceed, but I will take appropriate action tomorrow. And please note - you are just five, not six, I will remember.*" He got into his car and took off.

"*We were six when we started right? Where and who is the sixth one,*" I asked.

Krishna came running with a smile on his face. "*Hey, I am the 6th one.*"

"*You bastard,*" shouted everyone. "*Where the fuck were you hiding?*"

"*I was right behind you, hiding behind that milestone,*" explained Krishna with a smile.

"*Shame on you. It's good that Mr. Sparrow didn't find you, else it would have been a huge blow to the reputation of our batch. Now that you are not a part of five, as per Mr. Sparrow, you can go back to school and watch Speed Dancer,"* I recommended.

Krishna cut a sorry face. But nobody was happy with what he just did. He felt ashamed of his behavior. The problem was, he was always in the good books of the management and he didn't want to lose face. He didn't understand that living one's life was not about impressing others at the cost of our own natural self. Kaalia on the other hand knew the art of balancing the yin and yang.

That night in spite of Mr. Sparrow's show spoiler, we enjoyed our spicy dinner and the movie.

We were summoned the next day. Surpringly, we didn't get the severe upbraiding we had expected. After a quiet counselling and warning we were let off much to our surprise.

After this incident we judiciously kept away from Mr. Sparrow. After a few days, on a Friday night, we were discussing the cross-country scheduled for the next day.

Kamal fretted; *"Boys we are going to see stars tomorrow!"* referring to the cross-country.

"Is the cross-country scheduled for the night?" joked Virat.

"Nonsense."

"You said stars, didn't you?" explained Virat.

We thrashed Virat in mock anger, throwing a blanket over him.

"Virat, I think you have seen stars quite clearly," I alleged. Everyone had a hearty laugh.

"Hey, this time around I want to have fun in the cross-country." It was B.K. who was an ace athlete and the champion of the cross-country. *"Let's do one thing. We will have a challenge as to who will finish last - out of the two of us."*

I accepted the challenge. *"Ok. Let's do it."*

The race began. Unlike the usual B.K. who flies through a race, this time he was lazily sauntering with me. He pretended to run as if he was swimming against a powerful stream.

B.K. was witnessing the cross-country race for the first time. He was so focused on his run that he had never noticed the struggle of those who were putting in their best efforts to complete the race in time. Students were panting while running. They couldn't run continuously beyond 500 meters at a stretch and were walking. He felt as if he was on a picnic. I had a brisk walk with Kaalia for some time and then with B.K and some others.

B.K. felt he could have completed two cross-country at his regular speed. He missed running. The race didn't matter to me. I sensed that it mattered to B.K.

B.K. said, *"I think I have given my best now; I know you won't budge."*

I replied, *"Clearly you are the winner in this challenge because you gave up your medal for this game between us. All that I have lost is a Token of 50. I may still get a 30 now. You go ahead and run your race."*

B.K ran and got to Token 50. It was the lowest number in his entire schooling career. I got 31. We both completed our race within time. I told B.K., *"I know I can never beat you in your game. I sincerely appreciate your efforts in trying to beat me at mine."* We laughed.

The biology batch always looked forward to getting a free period. We either wished that the teacher does not turn up or that she'd be late for any reason. One such day there was no teacher in class and we were lost in fun. Out of nowhere, Mr. Sparrow entered the room.

"No!!!" we murmured.

He looked at me. I was busy poking Suri as usual. *"So, Mr. Ramakrishna, who is participating in the debate from your class?'*

"Debate? When is that Sir?"

"So, don't you even know that there is a debate scheduled this Saturday?"

"Sir, you know I generally don't look at notice boards. So I'm not aware of this," I replied.

Everyone started laughing.

"What do you normally looka at then?" asked Mr. Sparrow.

"Newspaper."

I regretted it immediately and tried to retract by saying, *"But for the past week I haven't been following that as well."*

Mr. Sparrow gave a wicked smile. *"Well, I know that. So, who is participating in this debate competition? I know for sure Ramakrishna; you won't be interested. You don't even know that there is a debate this weekend. You don't care to read notice boards. What can anyone expect from you?"* outlined Mr. Sparrow with a crooked smile.

That smile powerfully burnt my heart, my liver, my kidneys, and every possible organ that breathed life into me. I decided to participate in the debate no matter what the topic was.

The moment Mr. Sparrow left, I asked, *"What's the topic for debate guys?"*

"Its Plebiscite in Kashmir," said Aswani.

"Plebiscite? Well, what does that mean, dude?" I asked Suri.

"You are asking the wrong person, dude" exclaimed Suri. We laughed.

"It doesn't matter what it means; I am going to participate in this debate," I declared.

"I knew it. That's like a Gladiator, my friend," praised Deepu.

My classmates backed me. But none of the Gladiators knew what plebiscite was!

I met Goyal and asked for his help in preparation on the topic. He was our school adjutant. A proud Mauryan, Goyal had a strong military demeanor right from his school days. His immaculate looks and impressive bearing made him a perfect fit for the appointment of adjutant, which vested in him the authority to ensure discipline and compliance to rules by all school students. However, what made Goyal more popular was his excellent command of the English language and his participation in English skits during Annual Cultural Programmes. I was particularly impressed by his mono-act in Class 11th on 'Doctor Faustus', a play by Christopher Marlowe, which retells the story of a doctor-turned-necromancer making pact with the devil to sell his soul in return for absolute power. Goyal had powerfully portrayed the emotions of the protagonist in the final hour preceding his eternal damnation which made him hugely popular in the school.

Goyal was happy to see that I had taken initiative to participate in the debate. "*Never doubt your abilities; Challenge your limits*," he said.

He explained in detail what *plebiscite* meant, and how it is related to the state of Kashmir. It was an eye-opener for me. The problem with our history textbooks was that they recorded details only till India attained independence. Nothing about India after Independence was taught. Moreover, history is read only from the perspective of scoring and not about how it is relevant in today's context. As a result, nobody had a keen interest in the subject.

But now after getting to know the narrative of Kashmir, post-independence I realized how ignorant I was. The debate was scheduled within two days from the day I learned about this.

On the day of the debate, the auditorium was full. The energy level of the audience was high and charged. With me on stage, they expected some fireworks. The contestants began debating one after the other. It was a very interesting topic with people arguing on both sides, whether Plebiscite was required or not in Kashmir. Each side had its own strength of arguments. It wasn't an easy choice to make.

It was my turn now. I began.

Though India was declared independent on 15th August 1947, there were so many groups still seeking their freedom within the country. So, at what cost have we gained independence?

Independence is viewed differently by different people. Post-independence in 1947, many of the Princely states were reluctant to give up claim over their territories. But eventually, they had to relent except for the Princely states of Kashmir, Hyderabad, and Junagadh. Annexation of Kashmir was particularly complex as its geographic disposition and Muslim majority population made it highly lucrative for Pakistan while India chose not to cede any more of its territory. Maharaja Hari Singh, the Hindu Ruler initially made a standstill agreement with India and Pakistan. However, the sudden invasion of Kashmir by Pashtun tribes backed by the Pakistan Military forced Maharaja to sign an instrument of accession with India on 26th Oct 1947.

Subsequently, Indian troops landed in Kashmir, which resulted in the first Indo-Pak war in the same year of Independence. Pakistan started claiming that, since the Maharaja of Kashmir had a standstill agreement with Pakistan, he couldn't take a unilateral decision in this matter. Prime Minister Pandit Jawahar Lal Nehru promised to settle the issue by means of a referendum. Accordingly, a UN resolution was passed on 13th August 1948, instructing both the countries to withdraw their forces from the state of Kashmir so that they could proceed with the referendum. This condition was never fulfilled by Pakistan and so the referendum never materialized.

India chose to give Kashmiri people space and freedom by introducing Article 370 which gave them adequate autonomy on most state matters until the dispute was settled by means of Plebiscite. Despite being so liberal, all the initiatives taken by India in resolving the crisis haven't yielded any significant outcomes. Over the decades, the situation has only worsened with no signs of peace in the near future. Both the countries today lack the will to implement a solution which is resulting in the prolonged deadlock over the Kashmir dispute.

In such a backdrop, is it wise or right to go in for a plebiscite to resolve this issue? How far is it practical? Well, all my fellow friends have expressed their opinions based on different factors, but I feel that, if we view Kashmir through the lens of its people and the value of their lives, we should go for plebiscite once Pakistan fulfills its obligation of removing its forces from Pakistan occupied Kashmir. If we view Kashmir through the lens of its lucrative Geography there is no point of return. It all depends on which side of the coin we are looking at.

The auditorium was quiet when I spoke. It exploded in applause. Mr. Sparrow couldn't control his excitement either. In that electrifying moment, I felt elated for choosing to participate in the debate. I was happy that I could prove my point, but more than that, I was glad I researched something so relevant.

We, the Gladiators were put through mock tests. In a way, we were compelled to get serious about exams and study hard. One such night everyone left the study hall except for Kamal. Suri, Deepu, and I were chatting in our dormitory. The lights were switched off. It was around 10:45 pm.

When the clock ticked 11:00 pm, Deepu saw Kamal turning off the lights in the study hall. Then as per Deepu's plan, we pretended to sleep. Kamal came into the dormitory and turned on the lights.

As he approached his bed, Deepu groaned, *"Who is it?"*

I replied, *"It must be Kamal."*

"It's 12:00pm and Kamal winds up by now," said Suri.

"Why don't you guys learn from Kamal?" said Deepu.

All this conversation was heard by Kamal. He was delighted that he was being praised. He said, *"Yeah guys. You guessed it right. It's me, Kamal."*

"But it is not yet 12:00pm," said Deepu.

"I have come here to pick up my Chemistry book. I am sorry for disturbing your sleep." He walked back to the study hall carrying his book.

We couldn't stop laughing. Others who were listening to our conversation laughed too. What Kamal didn't know was that he was conned to sit in the study hall for an extra hour.

I was readying for a bath the next day. I looked for my towel where I had left it. It was missing. I saw another towel in its place.

"My towel is missing dude."

"Okay, why don't you check with Harsha then," said Suri promptly.

I understood who had played mischief.

The towel on my bed was Harsha's. It was quite clear. Suri had exchanged them.

"Come on Rambo, take your towel from Harsha. It's as simple as that. Big deal for you?" challenged Suri.

I realized that this issue has caused an unnecessary fuss. This has to end. I walked up to Harsha with his towel and said *"Hey dude, here's your towel."*

"Here is yours." We were laughing now feeling foolish about ourselves.

"It was really unbelievable that we had stopped speaking to each other for 5-6 years, after being thick friends during 6th and 7th grade. I don't even remember the issue," said Harsha.

"Whatever it was, why didn't either of us break the ice?"

"How stupid of us!" said Harsha.

"Our stupidity has cost us five years of our friendship and the memories we could have made." We thanked Suri for bringing us together.

We do make mistakes, but the sooner we realize them, the better.

Suri commented, *"When you guys initially stopped talking, I thought that it will be over in a day or two, knowing the kind of bond you shared. But it didn't. I wish I had done this earlier."*

It's easy to lose a friend over a trivial issue. Is an issue more important than a friendship? We do what we do because of our identity with our ego. While progressing with life, we don't pay heed to what and whom we are losing on the way. Only time can tell, how foolish we have been after experiencing loss. It's always better to learn from others' mistakes as we don't live long enough to make all mistakes ourselves. We realized this after 5-6 years.

Board exams fast approaching. During games, the School Adjutant, Goyal was annoyed with the lack of discipline and tardiness of the junior houses in spite of the presence of a physical training instructor. So, he took them to task. He made them run three tracks and asked them to take a *Murga* position, all this in the presence of the physical training instructor who took it as an insult. He asked Goyal to stop.

Goyal politely told him, *"Sir, please let me do my duty else this will become their regular attitude."* His response didn't go down well with the instructor, who had earlier tenanted an instructor tenure at the prestigious National Defence Academy before joining our school recently. He was unaware of the official and 'unofficial' powers the school Prefects wielded over the students in such matters.

He shouted. *"Behave yourself, Goyal. Do you know whom you are speaking to?"*

"I very well know Sir, but there's nothing wrong which is being done here. As an Adjutant how else am I required to ensure discipline unless you want me to be a mute spectator," replied Goyal.

His tone further infuriated the instructor and he caught Goyal's collar. *"How dare you speak so arrogantly?"*

Never before was a school Adjutant so publicly humiliated. Goyal was appointed as the School Adjutant not just on account of sheer merit but his excellent previous track record. He was a House Prefect of Maurya House before and had discharged all duties perfectly. He had the distinction of representing the state of Andhra Pradesh in the Republic Day parade at New Delhi as part of NCC junior Division in the 9th grade and was the runner-up in the selection of All India Best NCC cadet. He had earned his position on merit.

Goyal couldn't bear the loss of face in front of his juniors. Blinded by a false sense of dignity and disgrace, he immediately held the collar of the physical training instructor. It was an open encounter and the juniors bowed their heads in silence. This reaction was never anticipated by the instructor who immediately released Goyal's collar. Everything happened in a flash. Before Goyal realized his mistake, the damage was already done. The instructor didn't speak a word and quietly left the place.

The seniors from class 11th and 12th began arriving at the ground. By the time they arrived, the news spread like a raging fire. The matter was escalated to Mr. Rao, Sparrow and Daku in no time. Goyal went blank. He realized that he got carried away by the events and had no idea how to deal with the consequences. One act of thoughtlessness is all it takes, for a hero to become a zero.

The physical training instructor in particular was depressed as he felt humiliated by a student younger than half his age. Everybody from class 12 was with Goyal as we understood that the incident was instigated by the instructor. We comforted him and expressed solidarity. He felt reassured, though deep down he was steeped in guilt and bitterly regretted his action.

In order to resolve the matter, the first step was to appease the instructor. Goyal went to the instructor's house along with the other Prefects from class 12. He was inside the house, alone and in no mood to speak to anyone. He curtly said, *"Please leave me alone. I'm in no mood to speak to you now."*

A word was sent to Goyal from the management. By the time he reached there, it was unilaterally decided by the management to debar him from the school for his act of indiscipline without any investigation into the matter. All attempts to convince the management fell on deaf ears as they felt it to be a direct attack on their authority. They had to set an example. Goyal pleaded that it happened in the spur of the moment and the physical altercation was actually initiated by the instructor. But his pleading went unheard. Goyal, who was one of the most respected and powerful among the school Prefects, who was an inspiration for the juniors just an hour ago, found himself helpless. Most of us get carried away by emotions, unaware of where they would land us. After the storm passes, we are left to deal with the remnants.

Goyal returned heartbroken. The moment we saw him, we could sense the outcome of the meeting. We tried consoling him and promised to do whatever it takes to resolve it.

"There is nothing left to resolve. I'm debarred from the school," Goyal said sadly.

"What? That's crazy, how can they do it? Let's go back and talk to them!"

"I don't think they will budge. Our instructor has made up his mind not to soften his stand."

"In that case, let's go to him again," I reiterated. *"It's better only if a few of us go,"* said Goyal. So, Suri, Yagna, Kamal, and Virat went along with Goyal. As they went to him, he was not even willing to open his door. He said, *"Please leave. I can't help. I'm doing the least harm I could for the kind of humiliation you have put me through."*

"Sir, I'm sorry for what I have done. But I sincerely plead you to forgive me," pleaded Goyal.

Suri added, *"Sir, we never had any kind of animosity towards you. It was very unfortunate that this tussle happened Sir."*

"Please think of his future, Sir," begged Yagna.

"We are like your children, Sir. Please consider our actions as the one out of ignorance, Sir" requested Kamal.

All five pleaded with the instructor for over an hour. Though the instructor was very reluctant initially, he seemed to have softened his stance after much persuasion.

He sounded hurt, *"I can't totally forgive him. Whatever the situation might have been, I'm your instructor and you are my students. Can the dignity of the student be greater than his teachers?"* asked the instructor.

"Certainly not, Sir. We have grown up in this environment over the past six years and we have only been acting as per our school customs and never thought if our actions were inappropriate. Now we understand, how foolish we were, Sir," explained Goyal.

The instructor could sense Goyal's repentance. *"I'll speak to the administrative authorities and put forth my views. I can't forgive you in toto but I'll try to get your level of punishment reduced from debarment."*

"Thank you so much, Sir," they replied in unison and left.

We were waiting for the group to return. Looking at Goyal we sensed that there is some hope. We sat together discussing how one action led to the other. I observed, *"We act based on our thoughts, which are baseless in themselves."*

"Wow! I think we can sum up our entire journey with that line," added Kaalia.

Just then, Mr. Toms came in. *"Ada- Goyal, they have converted your rustication into suspension."*

We were all relieved.

"I can't thank God enough," rasped Goyal.

"Suspension for how many days Sir?" enquired Goyal.

"Four months; but you will be permitted to give the Board Exams," stated Mr. Toms with a sorry face.

The room was silent.

Breaking the silence, Goyal breathed, *"No worries, guys. I'm happy that at least I can appear for the Board."*

"That's the spirit Goyal, I replied. You are smart enough to understand the subjects on your own. Moreover, you need not go back home."

"Yes! You can stay outside the school and stay connected with us and we can have regular interaction," declared Suri.

"That's right!" agreed a relieved Goyal. *"Even I was thinking of the same so that my parents won't feel let down."*

Coming from a coaching center close by, Goyal and Suri had good connections with the local people, and more importantly their coaching teacher. On informing him about the situation he agreed to arrange food and accommodation for Goyal. He began staying outside the school but was in constant touch with us and started preparing on his own for the upcoming NDA and board exams.

NDA exam was fast approaching. Majority of the boys from the biology batch were confident of clearing the SSB but weren't confident about clearing the entrance exam. So, the entire responsibility of ensuring that we Gladiators pass our entrance exam fell on the shoulders of the toppers of the batch. On a thorough analysis of the previous year's question papers, we understood that they followed a particular pattern.

After critically analyzing, we could decode the structure of the question paper. The question paper had 120 questions in all with four sets A, B, C, and D. The first question for set A was the 31st question for set B, was the 61st for set C, and was the 91st for set D, and likewise. Based on this pattern everybody purchased a white handkerchief with checks. It had exactly 120 squares on a single side and was neatly folded and pressed. On the left corner of the kerchief, the set number was to be mentioned based on which the person who gets the kerchief will decode his answers. Each square box is dotted in any of the four corners denoting A, B, C, or D in a cyclic order. It worked on a network system. One kerchief had to be passed to a minimum of 2 persons. Accordingly, different teams were formed on our own in groups. The kerchiefs were passed on to the chosen team boys if they were in the same exam hall. If not, they fixed a time during which they have to take a bio-break from their respective invigilators at the same time and pass it on to their teammate.

We undertook many mock tests so as to ensure that we don't go wrong in decoding the answers in the exam hall. Finally, we were in the exam hall. Nobody was prepared but everybody was confident. We never succumbed to pressure, irrespective of the outcome. Our confidence stemmed from our support system. Nobody ever felt that he was alone in the battle. Everybody cared for one another and tried to help. There was no second thought about this. This solidarity was the source of our strength and spirit.

With that kind of concern and commitment for each other, there was no looking back. Everything went smoothly as per the plan but for a few hiccups here and there. Few people couldn't deliver their kerchiefs as per the fixed timelines; few were not allowed to take a bio-break by invigilators and few went wrong in decoding the codes. No matter how well-planned one is, 10% is bound to get messed and that's what happened.

Though the majority of us were happy with our performance in the NDA entrance exam, we were all more scared about the upcoming board exams. Only three months were left for our board exams but there was hardly any improvement in our results. An uneasiness gripped us after seeing our half-yearly exam results.

One morning as we went for our regular PT session, late by about 15 minutes as usual, we spotted Daku.

Yagna shouted, *"Make it fast now."*

After noticing Daku, all the seniors from classes 11th and 12th began walking briskly towards the ground.

Daku was standing calmly. *"Stop!"* he ordered.

As we began mumbling, he called out, *"Come here, you dog-bite fellow."*

Everyone laughed out loud.

I muttered, "*I don't know why this fellow is so fond of dog-bite,*" and walked towards him.

"*Good morning, Sir.*" I wished him.

"*Well, Good Morning, Mr. Ramakrishna, I was wondering which is your native place?*"

I smiled, "*I am from Kondrapole Sir.*"

"*Oh, I see! I was under the impression that you were from Rajahmundry,*" replied Daku.

I was suspicious as to why was he referring to Rajahmundry.

"*Well Mr. Ramakrishna, if you are from Kondrapole, please explain to me how your progress reports are going to Rajahmundry.*"

I had no words and stood in complete silence.

	Class XII
Chapter **17**	**Part III – Gripping Fear of Failure**

"*Never mind, I won't ruin your morning. We will meet in my office post-breakfast today,*" Daku left.

I stood there stunned taking in the ramifications of what happened. Our secret lay bare.

I realized, why our seniors were getting telegrams saying, "*COME HOME IMMEDIATELY,*" just a day before the exams. When I remembered what happened after my dog-bite issue, I felt we did it right by writing the wrong addresses. Moreover, the telegram trick couldn't be used so often for all the exams.

"*What was he saying, Rambo?*"

"*He wants to meet the Gladiators post-breakfast today.*"

"*Tell us something new! Anyway Why? What happened now?*" queried Suri.

"*Yeah, last time it was about our performances but this time it is about our postal addresses,*" I replied wearily.

"*What has he got to do with our addresses?*" Dhanu asked.

"Where has your first-semester progress report gone? Did it go to Vizianagaram or Visakhapatnam?"

"Oh, God! How did he figure it out?" Everyone looked around terrified to check if anyone overheard. As if it mattered now. I hadn't seen it coming when he asked me where I lived. None of us had given the correct address over the years, and now it had become a habit. I was worried.

"We even have Yagna-the school captain with us," laughed Suri.

"Well then, there is no point worrying. Let's hear what he has to say. No one will argue."

Later during the second period, we were summoned to Daku's den. The list was extensive. The entire army of Gladiators was there, except for one or two. We shrugged. Unity is strength. Though we were squirming inside, we weren't showing it. Nobody panicked.

"What a mastermind. How did he know?"

"I bet it was not Daku who found out," speculated Suri.

"It is not about who found out. It is about getting caught now; during the last leg of the school term, you idiot!" I hollered.

Post-breakfast about twenty Gladiators stood inside Daku's den. It was the first time we showed some shame. Our heads were bowed and our feet still. Daku was in total control.

"So, are you really ashamed to send your progress reports home?" enquired Daku.

Silence.

"I see even the school captain here! How remarkable, Mr. V. Y!"

"He too is a Gladiator Sir," I murmured.

"Who's that?" shouted Daku.

"When you are so ashamed of your performances, why do you show off so much? You shameless idiots," barked Daku.

"When he knows we are shameless, why the hell is he asking?" Dinu murmured.

"You are all keeping your parents in the dark by not sending them your progress reports. You are avoiding all chances of course correction. You are only ruining your progress," Daku continued.

We were silent. *"In a way, by not sending your progress reports to your homes you have sown a seed of your regress. Knowing that your parents won't see your report cards, you have become irresponsible and arrogant."*

"I am deeply hurt by the way you have been cheating your parents," thundered Daku. *"I will not let this continue. Your parents need to be informed about your performances. Only when they are aware, you will really make progress."* We knew he was right and he decreed it in our own interest but the situation wasn't apt we felt. We wanted to perform well and then inform them. If our parents learned of all this now, it would become an emotional issue, and that too just before the board exams.

Daku was restless. *"I am going to talk to all of your parents. There is no point in speaking to you people. Now get out all of you,"* he shouted.

"Oh, God! What do we do now? Speaking him out of this seems impossible," said Yagna.

We walked out of his office. We had to talk Daku out of this and buy ourselves some time to prepare for the exams. We need to first score well to save ourselves from any embarrassment.

"If that's the case we need to get to the parent of a local student today itself," said Suri.

"Why someone else's parent Suri? Why not your father? We can tell your father. He is quite supportive as well," I explained.

"Yes. That's true but he is out of station," replied Suri.

We looked at Dhanu. *"Oh no! Not mine,"* gasped Dhanu.

"Look, your house is close by and your father can reach here within an hour." We explained. *"I am quite sure Daku will calm down the moment he rants at any one of our parents."*

Dhanu couldn't say no, and in the interest of everyone he called up his father, who reached school within two hours from his call.

Dhanu entered the den with his father. Daku was not expecting anyone. As soon as Dhanu introduced his father, Daku rushed into a barrage of angry words. It was as though a dam had burst. He was in no mood to listen. Dhanu's father stood mute as Daku continued his outpouring of Dhanu's activities as well as that of ours. After half an hour he seemed to calm down. He had finished. *"Now it's up to you how you are going to handle your son. I have fulfilled my responsibility in keeping you informed of his progress."*

Daku spoke in English. Dhanu's father didn't understand a word. But he understood that his son had performed badly. Very sorrowfully he took Daku's leave. While leaving he told Dhanu, *"I couldn't follow what he said, my son. But I could make out that you failed. Never mind, do well this time."* Dhanu hugged his father and sobbed. He repented and promised to make up.

We were dismayed. All of us went to Dhanu's father and promised him that we will do our best and will not let down our parents. He left wishing everyone luck. Dhanu was happy that his father couldn't follow what Daku said, but he was still hurt that his father had to suffer the onslaught of Daku's anger.

We decided to work hard and formed groups for studying. The teams we formed while preparing for the NDA entrance exam, worked fine for our board exams as well. For most of us, it was a new beginning. We hardly knew the syllabus or even what was taught so far. Everything seemed to be new. In mathematics, we knew differentiation and integration only as terms and didn't know what they meant. The same was the case in almost all the subjects.

In my case, I was neither able to comprehend nor memorize, because I had accepted that I can't understand anything. This was the case with the majority of us. It was a herculean task for our team leads to keep us inspired and motivated. Kaalia was instrumental in keeping me confident. Other toppers chipped in to teach the rest of the class.

Just then, the results of the NDA written exam were announced. Almost all of us had passed. These results gave us the confidence to work harder. We knew how pathetic it would be if we cleared the SSB and failed class 12th board exams. We began studying seriously.

By then Gaurav and I had completed the storyline for Salman Khan's movie. We had spent at least 50-60 hours working on the script, sitting in isolation on the rooftops or inside the mango orchard. We had written the script on paper and audio-recorded the story on tape. I announced the title of our story SHIKAR-THE HUNT with a tag line, *in search of…* the plot was an action-adventure drama based on Indo-China and Pak backdrop. The plot took everyone by surprise.

Nobody imagined that we could come up with such an innovative storyline. After a thunderous response from our classmates, we posted the audiotape and our handwritten script to Salman Khan's address with great celebration.

As the board exams neared, the mock tests kept on increasing. Though we put in our heart to understand the subject, the concepts went too tough to grasp in a last-minute study. There was hardly any improvement in our performances. Vineel - the architect of the underground cable connection, gave me amazing advice in dealing with mathematics.

"Rambo, never think of the question as a problem before solving it; just laugh at it."

"Wow! That much I can do," I replied. *"But who will solve the problem after that?"*

"The moment you laugh at it, the question is half-solved."

I was good at the first part but failed miserably in the second. Then Kaalia took charge and began teaching me right from the basics. Soon the textbooks began making sense to me.

Our chemistry teacher, Mr. Shankar kept on giving me some assignments or the other. He would ask me to write a few equations twenty or thirty times, for practice. I was annoyed with the assignments but had no choice but to write. I realized the importance of the practice later during the viva for my lab externals. Mr. Shankar was present during my laboratory test and viva. I found him watching me with satisfaction as I answered all questions posed to me by the external invigilator with glee. I smiled to convey my gratitude.

Meanwhile, the SSB interview process also began. The good news of Kaalia, Pradeep, Ramu, Gaurav, M.P., Arjun, Adi and others clearing their interviews began coming in. The success rate of our batch was the best the school had scored so far. It kept everyone inspired and motivated. Let's clear the board exams; we felt that clearing SSB shouldn't be a problem.

In this great euphoria came the biggest news that Goyal cleared the interview. It was splendid news. We were happy for him, not that we doubted his ability in clearing the SSB but the timing of his result before the board exams would give him relief from the pressure he was living in the past few months. Even the administration that suspended him celebrated his success.

As almost all the toppers of our class cleared the SSB. It didn't look like they wanted to work for any other entrance exams like IITs and EAMCET[14] for which they had been preparing simultaneously. It was a blessing for us too, as their only role now was to ensure that we clear our board exams.

The SSB interview for most of the Gladiators including Suri, Deepu, and me was scheduled post-board exams. As the board exams neared, the lights never went off; we studied through the night. It was now usual for us to sit late at night till 1:00 to 2:00 am.

[14.] EAMCET -state level entrance exams for Engineering and Medicals

Amidst all the preparation, a sore thumb still stood out - Biology. Kaalia was from computers and there was hardly anybody in the biology batch who could teach me Biology. Even the teachers began attending to us in the study hall till 11:00 pm. Personal issues were set aside; what mattered most was the performance of their students.

Only when the teachers started tutoring us individually, did they realize that we scored poorly because we lacked conceptual clarity! The teachers merely completed the syllabus as per the schedule. Now it was too late. So, they analyzed previous years' question papers and focused on frequently asked questions so that we could score enough to pass the exam.

It was 1:30 am, when Deepu and I were about to sleep, we saw Suri walking into the dormitory. We began our conversation.

"This time around, I think Suri will do phenomenally well," I assumed.

"Why just well, I think he will outdo many stalwarts. Look at his commitment; he is still in the study," observed Deepu.

Suri was within earshot.

"I was thinking- why should we depend on others? Why not our own Suri," I emphasized.

"I was thinking of the same," agreed Deepu.

Hearing our conversation Suri, went out and returned with a bamboo stick to trash both of us shouting, *"You fuckers! You want me to teach you? You jack asses!"* We laughed as we chased each other.

The noisy chatter of the day vanished at night. The nights were all about teas and studying. Mr. Toms was astonished to see how much we had changed and prayed for us. Gaurav had cleared the SSB but he was worried about passing the board. Beneath all the hard work and joy there was an underlying unread message, a message we all knew. Time is running. School life is ending. We would be leaving school shortly.

It was the night before the board exams were about to begin. Even after putting in all our efforts, we didn't look confident. So once again the onus was on the toppers to deliver the kerchiefs. This time around it wasn't the same kerchief that was used for the NDA entrance exam, but a plain one. There it was objective and here it was descriptive. The plan was, all the toppers will have to write the answers on the kerchiefs and pass them on to their teammates.

All the questions remained the same for everyone in the exam. But they only differed in order for different sets. The only problem was in identifying the question to which that answer belonged. It was like reverse engineering.

To pass the kerchief to our friends who sat at a distance from us was another issue. We requested and cajoled our sub-staff members to pass on the kerchiefs while serving us tea during the exam. By tea-time, answers would be kept ready written on the kerchiefs. They were told not to serve tea randomly. They had to follow a particular order so that the kerchief can be passed safely.

Luckily for us, board exams were conducted in our school itself. There were two to three external invigilators. The other invigilators were our school staff members. It was all about evading the eyes of the invigilators so that we could carry out our plan. The only exam where nobody had to worry about anybody was English. It was like a Sunday among the exams. Thank God there was at least one subject where nobody had to worry about tracking the kerchief.

When it came to chemistry, all the equations looked similar to me. Though I got my kerchief from Kaalia I wasn't sure which answer belonged to which question. So, I just jotted down the answers without mentioning the question numbers as I thought that the evaluator who corrects my answer sheet might think that I actually forgot to mention question numbers in a hurry. *Since the evaluator knows which answer belongs to which question, he will give marks,* I thought and just copied the answers in the order on the kerchief without mentioning question numbers.

Those who didn't understand this logic went on to put question numbers for answers and lost their score. None of us aimed to score high. We only wanted to pass. Nobody was looking at the question paper; we were waiting for the kerchief.

As the invigilators were busy conversing among themselves, we were successful in passing the supplements.

We had successfully completed four papers by then i.e., English, mathematics, physics, and chemistry. Now only one optional paper was left i.e., computers/biology. Kaalia was from Computers and I from Biology. I didn't have the foresight to see this coming before opting for Biology. Kaalia felt sorry for me. But nothing could be done. The computers examination ended before the biology paper.

Biology was the last and the most crucial paper for the entire Biology batch; especially for me. There were very few from whom the kerchief could be expected; the needy were too many. So, I had to make some kind of alternative arrangement. The seating arrangement was as per roll numbers. Victor, who sat in front of me, was good at Biology.

So, the night before the Biology exam, I went up to Victor and requested him to help me out. Without even giving a second thought Victor agreed. I was relieved and informed Kaalia that Victor has promised to help me. I didn't bother to revise and completely relied on Victor though Kaalia advised me to study. I spent the night chatting with cadets and my friends from computers.

During breakfast, I went up to Victor confidently for assurance and went to the exam hall with great enthusiasm. A bell rang after the first 30 minutes. I had not begun writing. I was looking around to see what was happening. Everybody seemed to be in a state of panic.

"Damn, I should have taken Computers!" I thought for a second.

I looked at Suri, Deepu, Dhanu, and Dinu. Except for Deepu, the other three were smiling. I was passing time waiting for the kerchief from

Victor. Just then the bell rang signaling the completion of the first hour. I reached Victor's leg with my shoe and poked him. Victor moved his legs away. I looked around for the invigilator and then slowly called out, "*Hey Victor.*"

Victor didn't respond. Time was passing. Half the exam time was over and there was no sign that Victor would help. I realized I was in deep trouble. I thought he didn't hear me. I stretched as much as I could and whispered to Victor, but he was in no mood to listen. I bitterly said, "*You bastard! I will see you, if I don't pass this exam.*"

For the first time, Victor turned around and said, "*I am sorry dude, even I am struggling to answer these questions.*"

Life shows us our place when, we either undermine the power of others or feel overconfident about ourselves. "*Fuck you, you arsehole,*" I grumbled in disgust and helplessness.

Only the last one hour was left. I looked around for help. Just beside him in about 2 meters was Dinu, who understood what I was going through.

He gestured for my attention, "*Hey Rambo here you go.*" He threw an eraser with bits written over it in the tiniest writing.

I grabbed it and scribbled them in no time and again without putting any serial numbers. Then Dinu, kept his answer sheet at the edge of his table so that I could see it. But I couldn't see it clearly.

Then I kicked Victor on his back and taunted, "*You don't need to share anything with me, but at least for God's sake put your answer sheet to the right corner of your table.*" Finally, Victor obliged and kept his paper to his right.

Only thirty minutes were left. I had no time to lose. I began scribbling whatever I could see before the final bell rang. My hands were trembling while handing over my answer sheet to the invigilator. I was totally disappointed. Victor came up to me to say sorry. I didn't bother to look at him.

With that exam, my last memory of school became a nightmare. It didn't give me a moment of peace. The fear of failure began haunting me.

Chapter **18** : Embracing Karma

The last seven years of my school life flashed before me. I slowly opened my eyes and looked straight into those of Lord Rama.

Today, though I held my progress report, I didn't have enough courage to open it. All through my schooling, I have been known for my boldness. But I felt petrified now.

Where did I go wrong?

No No! Where did I go right?

Right and wrong are simply biases in our heads.

So, how did I become what I am - from what I was?

I was one of the first persons from our village, to join an English medium school. My mother always wanted me to become an IAS officer. I too presumed, I would be one soon.

I never hesitated in making promises to anyone. I was confident that I would keep my word. I never doubted my abilities as I felt that Lord Rama was always with me. I would pretend to be his staunch devotee, the monkey God Lord Hanuman, by inserting a stick in the back of my trousers and imagining that I had grown a tail.

The joy I derived while chanting the name of Lord Rama was immeasurable. When I had started out, I wanted to live the ideals of Lord Rama and become a role model for others to emulate. I believed that it was because of my faith and positivity that I managed to capture the minds and hearts of everyone whom I came in contact with.

I had an aura around me. My friends felt confident and comfortable in my company. I had a hack for every problem. I narrated stories that would make them happy, joyful, and confident.

Life seemed like a miracle. I enjoyed every bit of it. I never got bogged down in fear or pressure because I was open to criticism.

I had a goal when I joined Sainik School. All those who joined the school had qualities required for cracking our school entrance exam. On admission, we were allocated different houses. Each house had its own tradition to uphold and we were expected to live up to it.

However, not everybody could make it. One was expected to be flexible, stretch themselves to deliver. We had different traits, attitudes, sensibilities, set of values and came from different socio-economic backgrounds. But we had one thing in common - *to make our parents and villagers proud of us.*

While progressing, few could adapt, few felt left-out, few became homesick and few others looked lost and confused. Our personalities evolved as per our perceptions. Some excelled in sports, some in academics, some in extracurricular activities and some turned out to be all-rounders. Few became introverts; few became street-smart, while few were lost to oblivion.

Grade 9 formed the Lakshman-rekha[15] in the school. Those students who were sent to their respective senior houses had to level up their game.

[15.] Lakshman-rekha - ethical limits or convention, crossing which may lead to undesirable consequences.

They had to evolve further as it was all about survival of the fittest and the smartest in senior houses. If we didn't level up, we could become scapegoats for the rest of our lives. So, we had to become a different us; we formed a new identity for ourselves.

No matter what the situation was, I always had a way out. My friends loved my gutsy, fearless and cocky attitude and I earned the nick-name Rambo. In the process everyone forgot my name *Ramakrishna*; Rambo was my new name. The name came with a tag. A tag of being bold, with an uncaring cocky attitude. I felt I had to live by it. I began living my new identity - `Rambo`.

I didn't even realize how I had transitioned from Kondrapole's Ramakrishna to Sainik School's Rambo. However, a common factor between these two was my fearless attitude. While being Rambo, I slowly gave up being Ramakrishna. This was the beginning of my steep fall; in the deep bottomless pit of ignorance.

As long I lived with my identity it gave a great kick and high. The problem with this process was that I forgot the base when I climbed the peak. When we became seniors, we would look down upon others almost like our seniors did. We wanted to rule. Reality struck us only when we had to move on to the next achievement. We ended in chaos because the growth we had imagined was no growth at all. When we sat back and read in between the lines, everything got clear.

Life is meant to learn not to complain.

The Lord blessed me with friends who loved me unconditionally. They saw my failure as theirs, my pain as theirs and my glory as theirs. Now I realize that it was The Lord, who was with me through them in every situation.

All the lessons learned while growing are important. We pay for the quality we lack. The sooner one understood this, the quicker he progressed.

Despite all our ruckus with our teachers, they were fond of our batch. They had never seen a batch so concerned for each other. Every issue was dealt with as a group and not at an individual level.

We didn't allow our tussles with a few teachers to spoil the equation with other teachers. We were incredible to most and notorious to few.

Our teachers were proud of us; of our achievements as a batch. We have set numerous all-time records for our school; in academics, sports, athletics, and NDA entrance exam. Ours was a dream batch.

We were loved both by our seniors and juniors. No challenge seemed out of bounds for us. Our core strength was our spirit of oneness. No matter how tough the situation was, our resilience was the reason our teachers were in awe of us.

In many ways, we stood as exemplary role models. Our escapades and winnings made to the folk-lores of our school. Teachers spoke of our unity and spirit of oneness. Our immediate juniors admired the strength of our spirit but couldn't emulate us. The administration tried many tricks to weaken our strength and spirit but it led to further strengthening our resolve to stay united.

Our school has given us the strength, confidence and willpower to assume any responsibility with courage and conviction. Growing is not only about learning; it's about taking a stand for what mattered. We never gave up, nor will we ever, that's the spirit we inculcated from our school.

The timetable of our school never gave any scope for anybody to be laid back. It was a continuous stream of one activity after another and at the same time, we had to manage calls from the seniors and play safe with them.

We were challenged to outdo ourselves every time. These seven years will always remain as the most dramatic, productive, challenging, joyful, emotional, adventurous, and inspiring roller coaster ride for everyone in our own ways.

All of us had learned our lessons. Karma has its own way of teaching. No matter how much anybody tries to teach us or show us the right path, our *EGO* auto rejects these by assuming false identities. Fortunate are the ones who realize how fortunate they are.

I understood that whatever had happened to me was in my best interest. I thanked the Almighty for having made me realize the ultimate truth. The fear of failure no longer bothered me.

I felt immensely grateful for my rich and abundant life, my family, friends and my teachers. What more could I ask for?

My eyes brimmed with tears of gratitude. I thanked Him for whatever he had given me. I remembered my father's words when I was selected to join the school. "*The entire realm of action ends in wisdom. We all have our part to play. Now go and play your best game.*"

I realized that I have played my part and I shouldn't fret over the results of my karma now. I had earned this wisdom, the long way. This wisdom will serve me always.

Action never ends; we must always choose to play our best game.

I opened the envelope to read my result.

The Report Card read:

PASS

There are no endings. Only new beginnings.

If YOU aren't HAPPY, it's NOT YOU.

– RAMAKRISHNA LUNAVATH

Made in the USA
Columbia, SC
18 April 2022

59135944R00143